This Book Belongs To

_____

_____

DIVE NO

DATE

DIVE GROUP

WEATHER CONDITIONS

AIR LEVEL

START bar / psi	END bar / psi
_____	_____

DURATION

TIME IN
:

TIME OUT
:

DIVE TIME
:

AVERAGE DEPTH

MAX DEPTH

LOCATION

LOCATION NAME

COUNTRY

EQUIPMENT

ADDITIONAL NOTES

DIVE CENTER / RESORT STAMP

INSTRUCTOR	AI / DM	BUDDY

DIVE NO

DATE

DIVE GROUP

WEATHER CONDITIONS

AIR LEVEL

START bar / psi	END bar / psi

DURATION

TIME IN   TIME OUT
:   :

DIVE TIME
:

AVERAGE DEPTH

MAX DEPTH

LOCATION

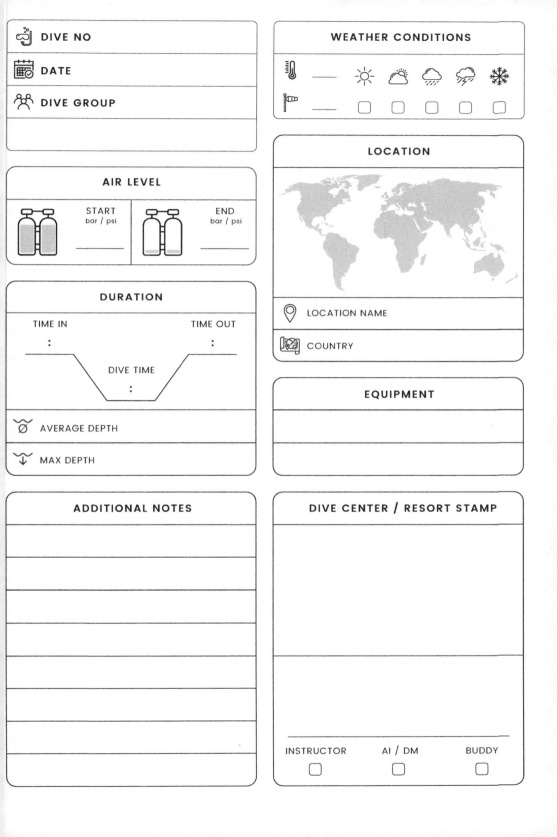

LOCATION NAME

COUNTRY

EQUIPMENT

ADDITIONAL NOTES

DIVE CENTER / RESORT STAMP

INSTRUCTOR   AI / DM   BUDDY

DIVE NO

DATE

DIVE GROUP

WEATHER CONDITIONS

AIR LEVEL

START bar / psi	END bar / psi

DURATION

TIME IN   :

TIME OUT   :

DIVE TIME   :

AVERAGE DEPTH

MAX DEPTH

LOCATION

LOCATION NAME

COUNTRY

EQUIPMENT

ADDITIONAL NOTES

DIVE CENTER / RESORT STAMP

INSTRUCTOR	AI / DM	BUDDY

DIVE NO

DATE

DIVE GROUP

WEATHER CONDITIONS

___

___

AIR LEVEL

START bar / psi	END bar / psi
_____	_____

DURATION

TIME IN   TIME OUT

:   :

DIVE TIME

:

AVERAGE DEPTH

MAX DEPTH

LOCATION

LOCATION NAME

COUNTRY

EQUIPMENT

ADDITIONAL NOTES

DIVE CENTER / RESORT STAMP

INSTRUCTOR   AI / DM   BUDDY

DIVE NO

DATE

DIVE GROUP

WEATHER CONDITIONS

AIR LEVEL

START bar / psi	END bar / psi
_____	_____

DURATION

TIME IN   TIME OUT

:   :

DIVE TIME

:

AVERAGE DEPTH

MAX DEPTH

LOCATION

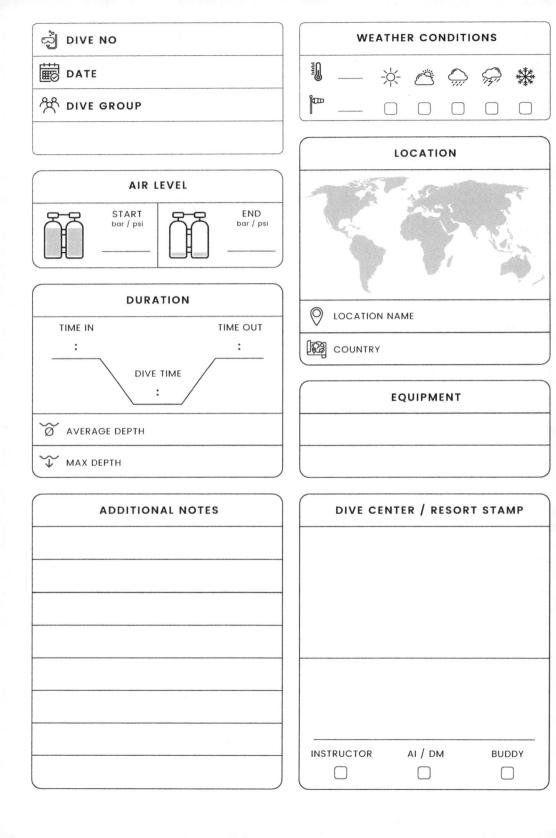

LOCATION NAME

COUNTRY

EQUIPMENT

ADDITIONAL NOTES

DIVE CENTER / RESORT STAMP

INSTRUCTOR   AI / DM   BUDDY

DIVE NO

DATE

DIVE GROUP

WEATHER CONDITIONS

AIR LEVEL

START
bar / psi

END
bar / psi

LOCATION

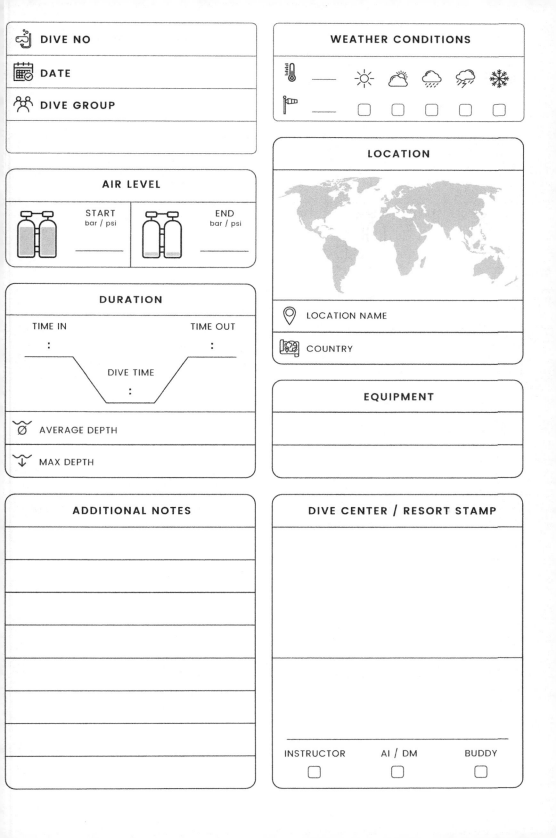

LOCATION NAME

COUNTRY

DURATION

TIME IN

TIME OUT

:

:

DIVE TIME

:

AVERAGE DEPTH

MAX DEPTH

EQUIPMENT

ADDITIONAL NOTES

DIVE CENTER / RESORT STAMP

INSTRUCTOR

AI / DM

BUDDY

DIVE NO

DATE

DIVE GROUP

AIR LEVEL

START bar / psi	END bar / psi
_____	_____

DURATION

TIME IN   TIME OUT

:   :

DIVE TIME

:

AVERAGE DEPTH

MAX DEPTH

WEATHER CONDITIONS

_____

_____

LOCATION

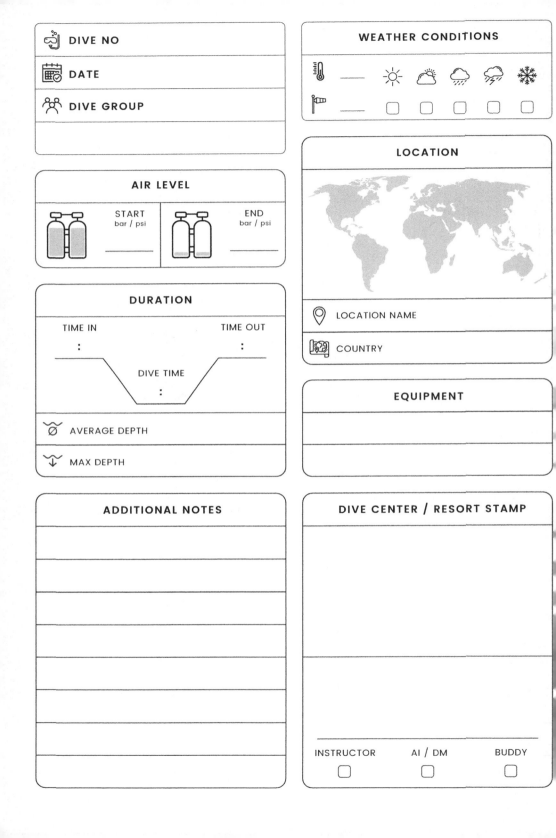

LOCATION NAME

COUNTRY

EQUIPMENT

ADDITIONAL NOTES

DIVE CENTER / RESORT STAMP

INSTRUCTOR   AI / DM   BUDDY

DIVE NO

DATE

DIVE GROUP

WEATHER CONDITIONS

AIR LEVEL

START
bar / psi

END
bar / psi

DURATION

TIME IN

TIME OUT

:

:

DIVE TIME

:

AVERAGE DEPTH

MAX DEPTH

LOCATION

LOCATION NAME

COUNTRY

EQUIPMENT

ADDITIONAL NOTES

DIVE CENTER / RESORT STAMP

INSTRUCTOR

AI / DM

BUDDY

DIVE NO

DATE

DIVE GROUP

WEATHER CONDITIONS

AIR LEVEL

START bar / psi	END bar / psi
_____	_____

DURATION

TIME IN   TIME OUT

:   :

DIVE TIME

:

AVERAGE DEPTH

MAX DEPTH

LOCATION

LOCATION NAME

COUNTRY

EQUIPMENT

ADDITIONAL NOTES

DIVE CENTER / RESORT STAMP

INSTRUCTOR   AI / DM   BUDDY

DIVE NO

DATE

DIVE GROUP

WEATHER CONDITIONS

AIR LEVEL

START bar / psi	END bar / psi

DURATION

TIME IN   TIME OUT
:   :

DIVE TIME
:

AVERAGE DEPTH

MAX DEPTH

LOCATION

LOCATION NAME

COUNTRY

EQUIPMENT

ADDITIONAL NOTES

DIVE CENTER / RESORT STAMP

INSTRUCTOR   AI / DM   BUDDY

DIVE NO

DATE

DIVE GROUP

WEATHER CONDITIONS

AIR LEVEL

	START bar / psi		END bar / psi
	_____		_____

LOCATION

LOCATION NAME

COUNTRY

DURATION

TIME IN   TIME OUT

:   :

DIVE TIME

:

AVERAGE DEPTH

MAX DEPTH

EQUIPMENT

ADDITIONAL NOTES

DIVE CENTER / RESORT STAMP

INSTRUCTOR   AI / DM   BUDDY

DIVE NO

DATE

DIVE GROUP

WEATHER CONDITIONS

AIR LEVEL

START bar / psi	END bar / psi
_____	_____

DURATION

TIME IN

TIME OUT

:

:

DIVE TIME

:

AVERAGE DEPTH

MAX DEPTH

LOCATION

LOCATION NAME

COUNTRY

EQUIPMENT

ADDITIONAL NOTES

DIVE CENTER / RESORT STAMP

INSTRUCTOR

AI / DM

BUDDY

DIVE NO

DATE

DIVE GROUP

WEATHER CONDITIONS

AIR LEVEL

START
bar / psi

END
bar / psi

DURATION

TIME IN

TIME OUT

:

:

DIVE TIME

:

AVERAGE DEPTH

MAX DEPTH

LOCATION

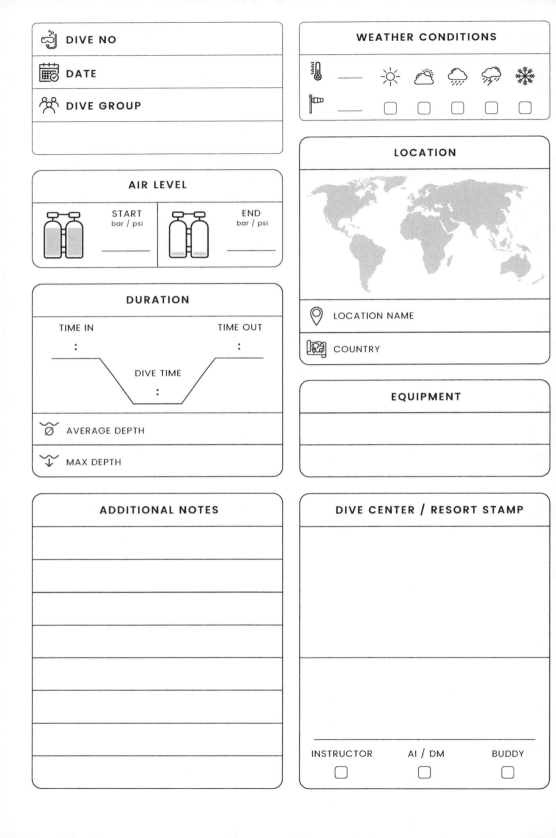

LOCATION NAME

COUNTRY

EQUIPMENT

ADDITIONAL NOTES

DIVE CENTER / RESORT STAMP

INSTRUCTOR

AI / DM

BUDDY

DIVE NO

DATE

DIVE GROUP

WEATHER CONDITIONS

AIR LEVEL

	START bar / psi		END bar / psi
	_____		_____

DURATION

TIME IN

:

TIME OUT

:

DIVE TIME

:

AVERAGE DEPTH

MAX DEPTH

LOCATION

LOCATION NAME

COUNTRY

EQUIPMENT

ADDITIONAL NOTES

DIVE CENTER / RESORT STAMP

INSTRUCTOR

AI / DM

BUDDY

DIVE NO

DATE

DIVE GROUP

WEATHER CONDITIONS

AIR LEVEL

	START bar / psi		END bar / psi
	_____		_____

DURATION

TIME IN

:

TIME OUT

:

DIVE TIME

:

AVERAGE DEPTH

MAX DEPTH

LOCATION

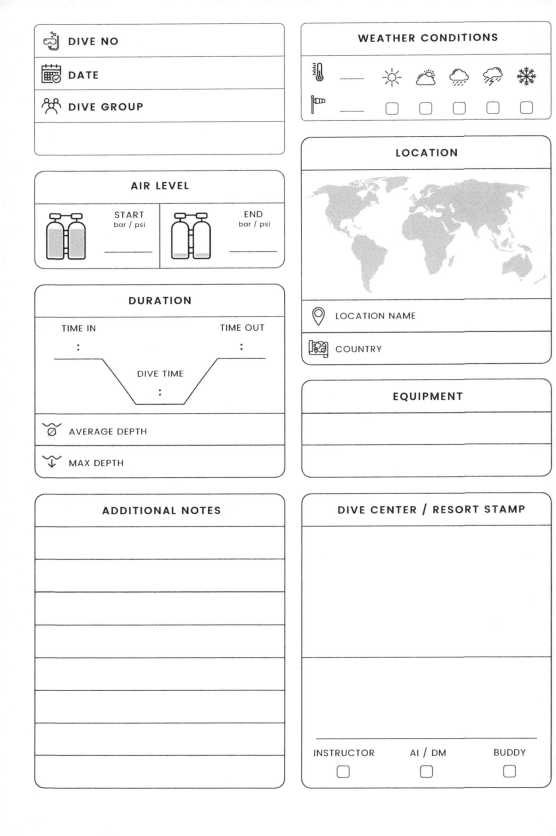

LOCATION NAME

COUNTRY

EQUIPMENT

ADDITIONAL NOTES

DIVE CENTER / RESORT STAMP

INSTRUCTOR   AI / DM   BUDDY

DIVE NO

DATE

DIVE GROUP

WEATHER CONDITIONS

AIR LEVEL

START bar / psi	END bar / psi
_____	_____

DURATION

TIME IN
:

TIME OUT
:

DIVE TIME
:

AVERAGE DEPTH

MAX DEPTH

LOCATION

LOCATION NAME

COUNTRY

EQUIPMENT

ADDITIONAL NOTES

DIVE CENTER / RESORT STAMP

INSTRUCTOR   AI / DM   BUDDY

DIVE NO

DATE

DIVE GROUP

WEATHER CONDITIONS

AIR LEVEL

START
bar / psi

END
bar / psi

DURATION

TIME IN

TIME OUT

:

:

DIVE TIME

:

AVERAGE DEPTH

MAX DEPTH

LOCATION

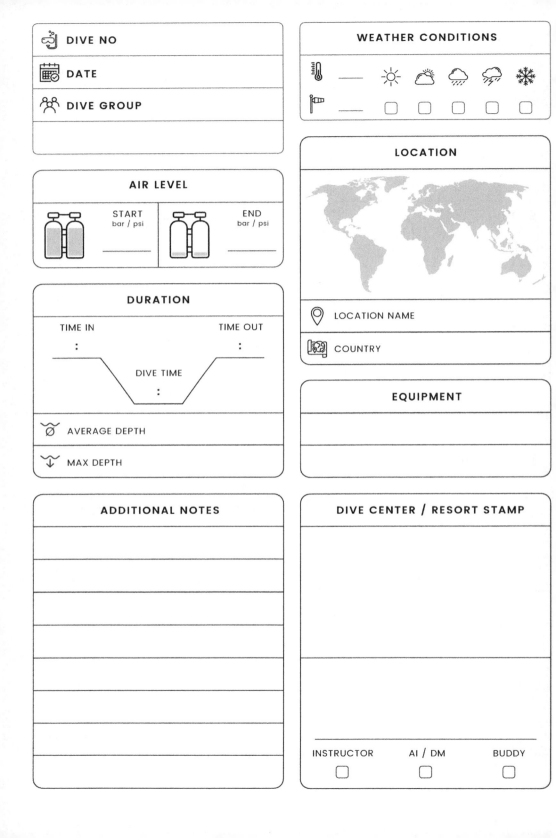

LOCATION NAME

COUNTRY

EQUIPMENT

ADDITIONAL NOTES

DIVE CENTER / RESORT STAMP

INSTRUCTOR

AI / DM

BUDDY

DIVE NO

DATE

DIVE GROUP

WEATHER CONDITIONS

AIR LEVEL

START
bar / psi

END
bar / psi

LOCATION

LOCATION NAME

COUNTRY

DURATION

TIME IN

TIME OUT

:

:

DIVE TIME

:

AVERAGE DEPTH

MAX DEPTH

EQUIPMENT

ADDITIONAL NOTES

DIVE CENTER / RESORT STAMP

INSTRUCTOR

AI / DM

BUDDY

DIVE NO

DATE

DIVE GROUP

WEATHER CONDITIONS

AIR LEVEL

START bar / psi	END bar / psi
_____	_____

DURATION

TIME IN _:_

TIME OUT _:_

DIVE TIME _:_

AVERAGE DEPTH

MAX DEPTH

LOCATION

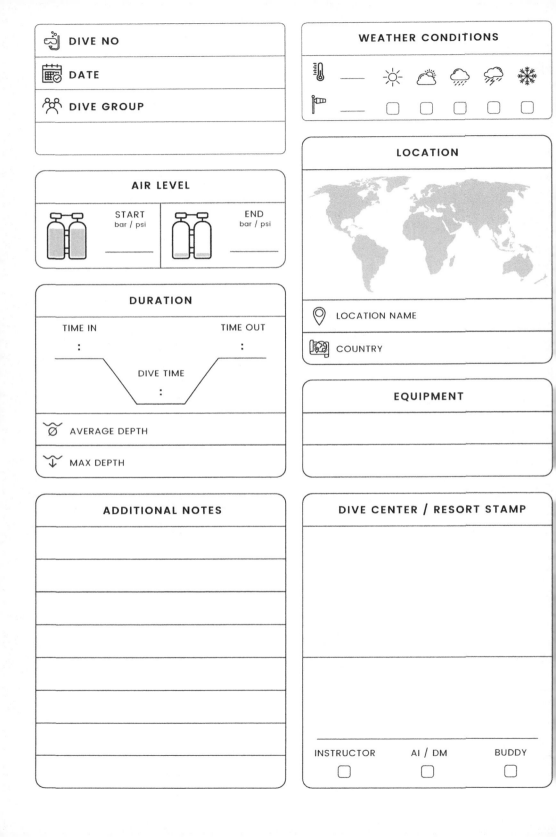

LOCATION NAME

COUNTRY

EQUIPMENT

ADDITIONAL NOTES

DIVE CENTER / RESORT STAMP

INSTRUCTOR ☐   AI / DM ☐   BUDDY ☐

DIVE NO

DATE

DIVE GROUP

WEATHER CONDITIONS

AIR LEVEL

START
bar / psi

END
bar / psi

DURATION

TIME IN

TIME OUT

:

:

DIVE TIME

:

AVERAGE DEPTH

MAX DEPTH

LOCATION

LOCATION NAME

COUNTRY

EQUIPMENT

ADDITIONAL NOTES

DIVE CENTER / RESORT STAMP

INSTRUCTOR

AI / DM

BUDDY

DIVE NO

DATE

DIVE GROUP

AIR LEVEL

START
bar / psi

END
bar / psi

DURATION

TIME IN

TIME OUT

:

:

DIVE TIME

:

AVERAGE DEPTH

MAX DEPTH

WEATHER CONDITIONS

LOCATION

LOCATION NAME

COUNTRY

EQUIPMENT

ADDITIONAL NOTES

DIVE CENTER / RESORT STAMP

INSTRUCTOR

AI / DM

BUDDY

DIVE NO

DATE

DIVE GROUP

WEATHER CONDITIONS

AIR LEVEL

START bar / psi	END bar / psi
_____	_____

DURATION

TIME IN   TIME OUT

:   :

DIVE TIME

:

AVERAGE DEPTH

MAX DEPTH

LOCATION

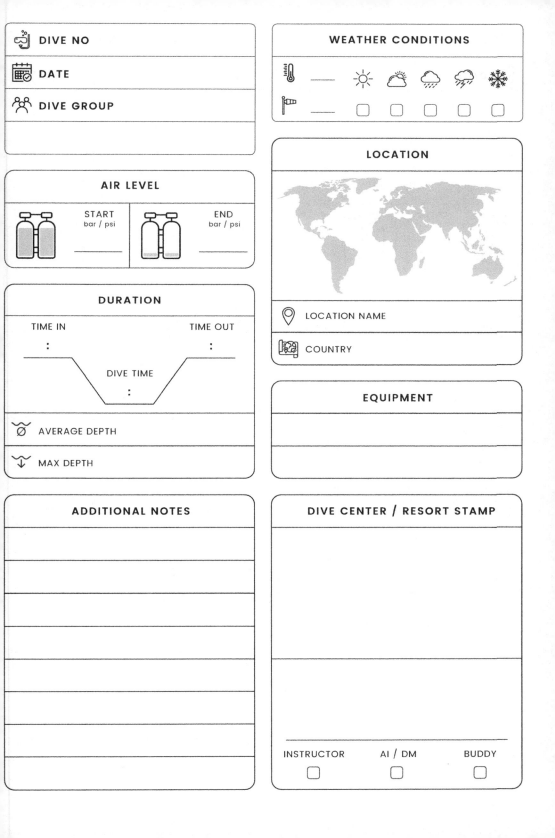

LOCATION NAME

COUNTRY

EQUIPMENT

ADDITIONAL NOTES

DIVE CENTER / RESORT STAMP

_____

INSTRUCTOR   AI / DM   BUDDY

DIVE NO

DATE

DIVE GROUP

AIR LEVEL

START
bar / psi

_____

END
bar / psi

_____

DURATION

TIME IN

:

TIME OUT

:

DIVE TIME

:

AVERAGE DEPTH

MAX DEPTH

WEATHER CONDITIONS

___

___

LOCATION

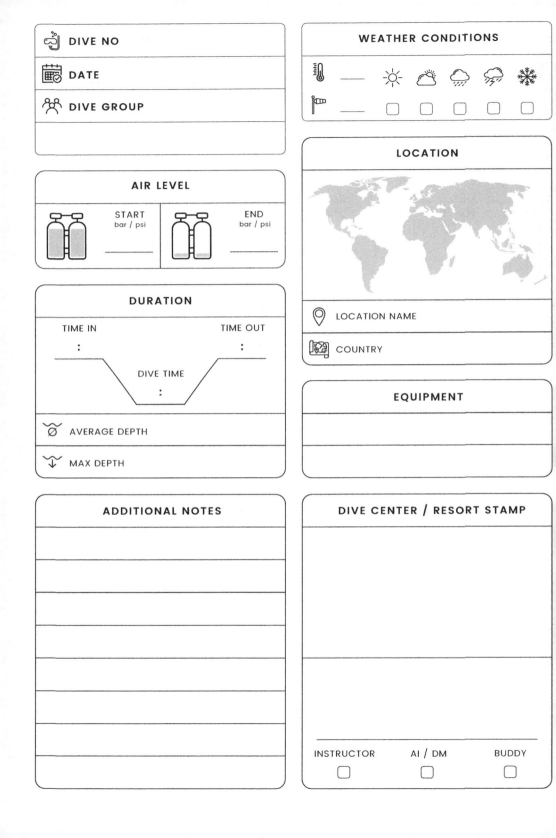

LOCATION NAME

COUNTRY

EQUIPMENT

ADDITIONAL NOTES

DIVE CENTER / RESORT STAMP

INSTRUCTOR

AI / DM

BUDDY

DIVE NO

DATE

DIVE GROUP

WEATHER CONDITIONS

AIR LEVEL

START bar / psi	END bar / psi
_____	_____

DURATION

TIME IN   TIME OUT

:   :

DIVE TIME

:

AVERAGE DEPTH

MAX DEPTH

LOCATION

LOCATION NAME

COUNTRY

EQUIPMENT

ADDITIONAL NOTES

DIVE CENTER / RESORT STAMP

INSTRUCTOR   AI / DM   BUDDY

DIVE NO

DATE

DIVE GROUP

WEATHER CONDITIONS

AIR LEVEL

START	END
bar / psi	bar / psi

LOCATION

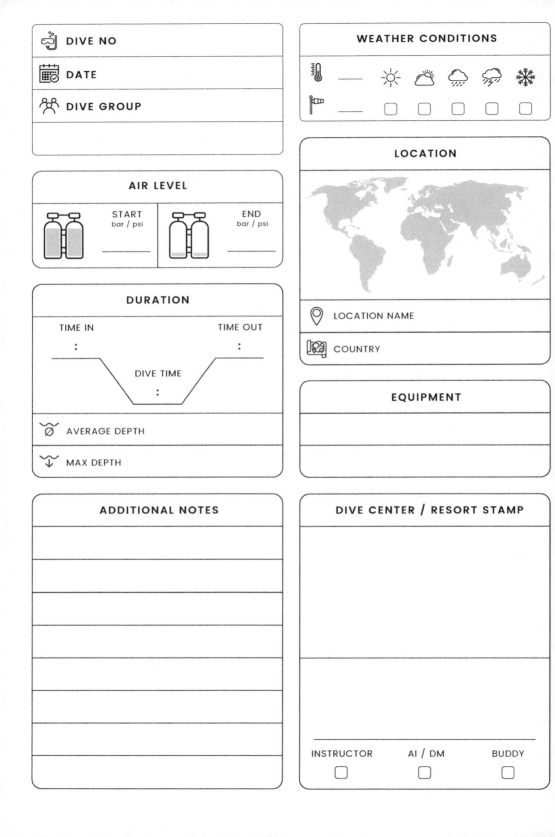

LOCATION NAME

COUNTRY

DURATION

TIME IN   TIME OUT

:   :

DIVE TIME

:

AVERAGE DEPTH

MAX DEPTH

EQUIPMENT

ADDITIONAL NOTES

DIVE CENTER / RESORT STAMP

INSTRUCTOR   AI / DM   BUDDY

DIVE NO

DATE

DIVE GROUP

WEATHER CONDITIONS

AIR LEVEL

START bar / psi	END bar / psi

DURATION

TIME IN   TIME OUT

:   :

DIVE TIME

:

AVERAGE DEPTH

MAX DEPTH

LOCATION

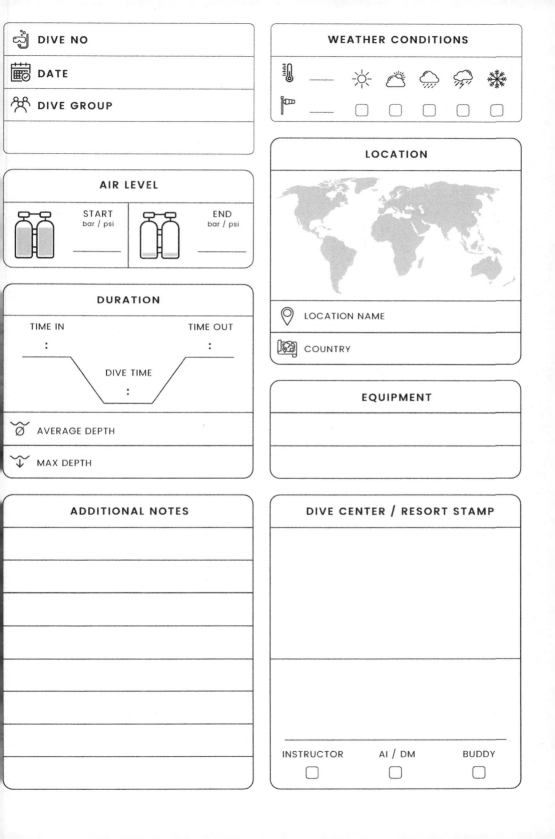

LOCATION NAME

COUNTRY

EQUIPMENT

ADDITIONAL NOTES

DIVE CENTER / RESORT STAMP

INSTRUCTOR   AI / DM   BUDDY

DIVE NO

DATE

DIVE GROUP

WEATHER CONDITIONS

AIR LEVEL

START
bar / psi

END
bar / psi

DURATION

TIME IN

TIME OUT

:

:

DIVE TIME

:

AVERAGE DEPTH

MAX DEPTH

LOCATION

LOCATION NAME

COUNTRY

EQUIPMENT

ADDITIONAL NOTES

DIVE CENTER / RESORT STAMP

INSTRUCTOR

AI / DM

BUDDY

DIVE NO

DATE

DIVE GROUP

WEATHER CONDITIONS

AIR LEVEL

START bar / psi	END bar / psi
_____	_____

DURATION

TIME IN   TIME OUT
:   :

DIVE TIME
:

∅ AVERAGE DEPTH

MAX DEPTH

LOCATION

© LOCATION NAME

COUNTRY

EQUIPMENT

ADDITIONAL NOTES

DIVE CENTER / RESORT STAMP

INSTRUCTOR   AI / DM   BUDDY

DIVE NO

DATE

DIVE GROUP

WEATHER CONDITIONS

AIR LEVEL

START
bar / psi

END
bar / psi

LOCATION

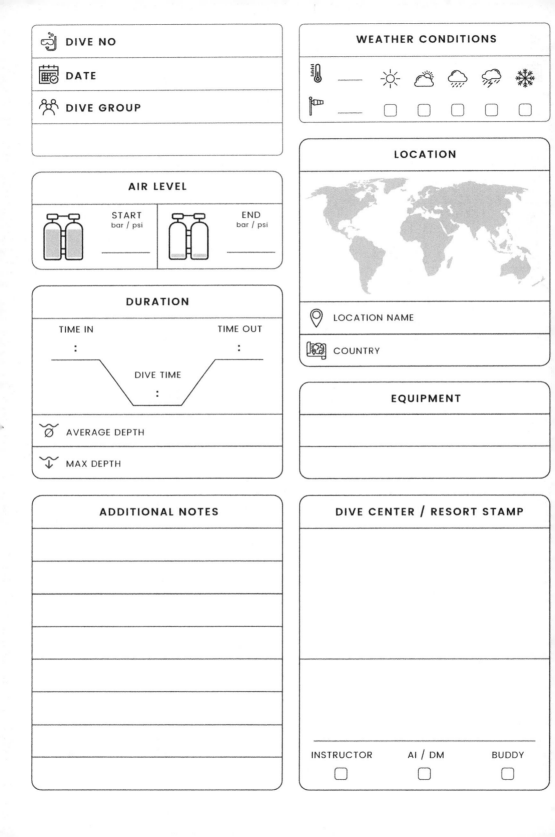

LOCATION NAME

COUNTRY

DURATION

TIME IN

TIME OUT

:

:

DIVE TIME

:

AVERAGE DEPTH

MAX DEPTH

EQUIPMENT

ADDITIONAL NOTES

DIVE CENTER / RESORT STAMP

INSTRUCTOR

AI / DM

BUDDY

DIVE NO

DATE

DIVE GROUP

WEATHER CONDITIONS

AIR LEVEL

START bar / psi	END bar / psi
_____	_____

DURATION

TIME IN

:

TIME OUT

:

DIVE TIME

:

AVERAGE DEPTH

MAX DEPTH

LOCATION

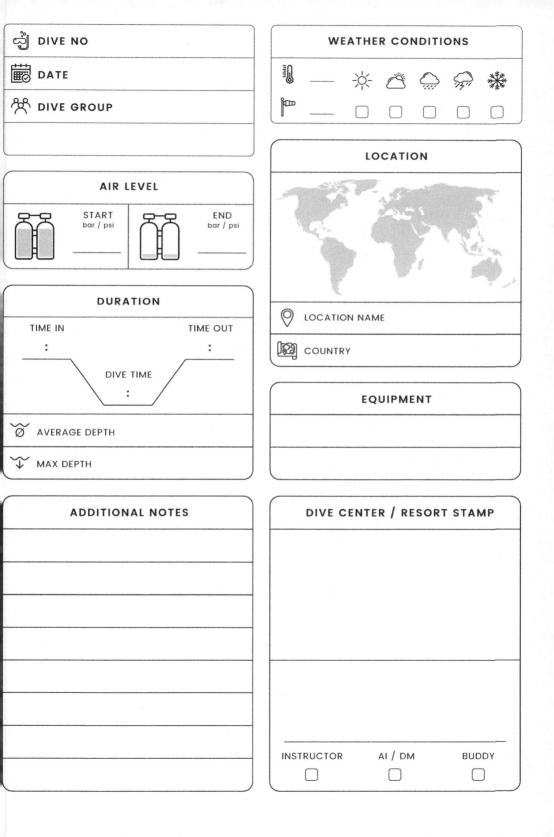

LOCATION NAME

COUNTRY

EQUIPMENT

ADDITIONAL NOTES

DIVE CENTER / RESORT STAMP

INSTRUCTOR	AI / DM	BUDDY

DIVE NO

DATE

DIVE GROUP

WEATHER CONDITIONS

AIR LEVEL

START bar / psi	END bar / psi

DURATION

TIME IN

TIME OUT

:

:

DIVE TIME

:

AVERAGE DEPTH

MAX DEPTH

LOCATION

LOCATION NAME

COUNTRY

EQUIPMENT

ADDITIONAL NOTES

DIVE CENTER / RESORT STAMP

INSTRUCTOR	AI / DM	BUDDY

DIVE NO

DATE

DIVE GROUP

WEATHER CONDITIONS

AIR LEVEL

START bar / psi	END bar / psi

DURATION

TIME IN   TIME OUT

:   :

DIVE TIME

:

AVERAGE DEPTH

MAX DEPTH

LOCATION

LOCATION NAME

COUNTRY

EQUIPMENT

ADDITIONAL NOTES

DIVE CENTER / RESORT STAMP

INSTRUCTOR   AI / DM   BUDDY

DIVE NO

DATE

DIVE GROUP

WEATHER CONDITIONS

AIR LEVEL

START bar / psi	END bar / psi

DURATION

TIME IN

TIME OUT

:

:

DIVE TIME

:

AVERAGE DEPTH

MAX DEPTH

LOCATION

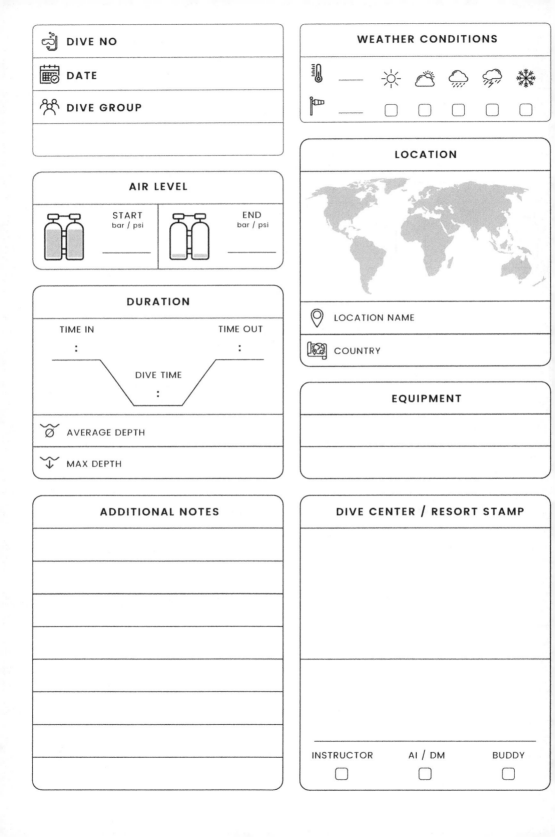

LOCATION NAME

COUNTRY

EQUIPMENT

ADDITIONAL NOTES

DIVE CENTER / RESORT STAMP

INSTRUCTOR	AI / DM	BUDDY

DIVE NO

DATE

DIVE GROUP

WEATHER CONDITIONS

AIR LEVEL

START bar / psi	END bar / psi
_____	_____

DURATION

TIME IN   TIME OUT

:   :

DIVE TIME

:

AVERAGE DEPTH

MAX DEPTH

LOCATION

LOCATION NAME

COUNTRY

EQUIPMENT

ADDITIONAL NOTES

DIVE CENTER / RESORT STAMP

INSTRUCTOR   AI / DM   BUDDY

DIVE NO

DATE

DIVE GROUP

WEATHER CONDITIONS

AIR LEVEL

	START bar / psi		END bar / psi

DURATION

TIME IN

TIME OUT

:

:

DIVE TIME

:

AVERAGE DEPTH

MAX DEPTH

LOCATION

LOCATION NAME

COUNTRY

EQUIPMENT

ADDITIONAL NOTES

DIVE CENTER / RESORT STAMP

INSTRUCTOR

AI / DM

BUDDY

DIVE NO

DATE

DIVE GROUP

WEATHER CONDITIONS

AIR LEVEL

START bar / psi	END bar / psi
_____	_____

DURATION

TIME IN   TIME OUT

:   :

DIVE TIME

:

AVERAGE DEPTH

MAX DEPTH

LOCATION

LOCATION NAME

COUNTRY

EQUIPMENT

ADDITIONAL NOTES

DIVE CENTER / RESORT STAMP

INSTRUCTOR   AI / DM   BUDDY

DIVE NO

DATE

DIVE GROUP

WEATHER CONDITIONS

AIR LEVEL

START bar / psi	END bar / psi

DURATION

TIME IN

TIME OUT

:

:

DIVE TIME

:

AVERAGE DEPTH

MAX DEPTH

LOCATION

LOCATION NAME

COUNTRY

EQUIPMENT

ADDITIONAL NOTES

DIVE CENTER / RESORT STAMP

INSTRUCTOR   AI / DM   BUDDY

DIVE NO

DATE

DIVE GROUP

WEATHER CONDITIONS

AIR LEVEL

START
bar / psi

END
bar / psi

DURATION

TIME IN

TIME OUT

:

:

DIVE TIME

:

AVERAGE DEPTH

MAX DEPTH

LOCATION

LOCATION NAME

COUNTRY

EQUIPMENT

ADDITIONAL NOTES

DIVE CENTER / RESORT STAMP

INSTRUCTOR   AI / DM   BUDDY

DIVE NO

DATE

DIVE GROUP

WEATHER CONDITIONS

AIR LEVEL

START bar / psi	END bar / psi
_____	_____

DURATION

TIME IN   TIME OUT

:   :

DIVE TIME

:

AVERAGE DEPTH

MAX DEPTH

LOCATION

LOCATION NAME

COUNTRY

EQUIPMENT

ADDITIONAL NOTES

DIVE CENTER / RESORT STAMP

INSTRUCTOR   AI / DM   BUDDY

DIVE NO

DATE

DIVE GROUP

WEATHER CONDITIONS

AIR LEVEL

START bar / psi	END bar / psi
_____	_____

DURATION

TIME IN   TIME OUT

:   :

DIVE TIME

:

AVERAGE DEPTH

MAX DEPTH

LOCATION

LOCATION NAME

COUNTRY

EQUIPMENT

ADDITIONAL NOTES

DIVE CENTER / RESORT STAMP

INSTRUCTOR   AI / DM   BUDDY

DIVE NO

DATE

DIVE GROUP

WEATHER CONDITIONS

AIR LEVEL

START bar / psi	END bar / psi
_____	_____

DURATION

TIME IN | TIME OUT

: | :

DIVE TIME

:

AVERAGE DEPTH

MAX DEPTH

LOCATION

LOCATION NAME

COUNTRY

EQUIPMENT

ADDITIONAL NOTES

DIVE CENTER / RESORT STAMP

INSTRUCTOR | AI / DM | BUDDY

DIVE NO

DATE

DIVE GROUP

WEATHER CONDITIONS

AIR LEVEL

	START bar / psi		END bar / psi

DURATION

TIME IN

:

TIME OUT

:

DIVE TIME

:

AVERAGE DEPTH

MAX DEPTH

LOCATION

LOCATION NAME

COUNTRY

EQUIPMENT

ADDITIONAL NOTES

DIVE CENTER / RESORT STAMP

INSTRUCTOR

AI / DM

BUDDY

DIVE NO

DATE

DIVE GROUP

WEATHER CONDITIONS

AIR LEVEL

START bar / psi	END bar / psi
_____	_____

DURATION

TIME IN | TIME OUT
: | :

DIVE TIME
:

AVERAGE DEPTH

MAX DEPTH

LOCATION

LOCATION NAME

COUNTRY

EQUIPMENT

ADDITIONAL NOTES

DIVE CENTER / RESORT STAMP

INSTRUCTOR | AI / DM | BUDDY

DIVE NO

DATE

DIVE GROUP

WEATHER CONDITIONS

AIR LEVEL

START
bar / psi

END
bar / psi

LOCATION

LOCATION NAME

COUNTRY

DURATION

TIME IN

TIME OUT

:

:

DIVE TIME

:

AVERAGE DEPTH

MAX DEPTH

EQUIPMENT

ADDITIONAL NOTES

DIVE CENTER / RESORT STAMP

INSTRUCTOR

AI / DM

BUDDY

DIVE NO

DATE

DIVE GROUP

WEATHER CONDITIONS

AIR LEVEL

START bar / psi	END bar / psi
_____	_____

DURATION

TIME IN   TIME OUT

:   :

DIVE TIME

:

AVERAGE DEPTH

MAX DEPTH

LOCATION

LOCATION NAME

COUNTRY

EQUIPMENT

ADDITIONAL NOTES

DIVE CENTER / RESORT STAMP

INSTRUCTOR   AI / DM   BUDDY

DIVE NO

DATE

DIVE GROUP

WEATHER CONDITIONS

AIR LEVEL

START
bar / psi

END
bar / psi

DURATION

TIME IN

TIME OUT

:

:

DIVE TIME

:

AVERAGE DEPTH

MAX DEPTH

LOCATION

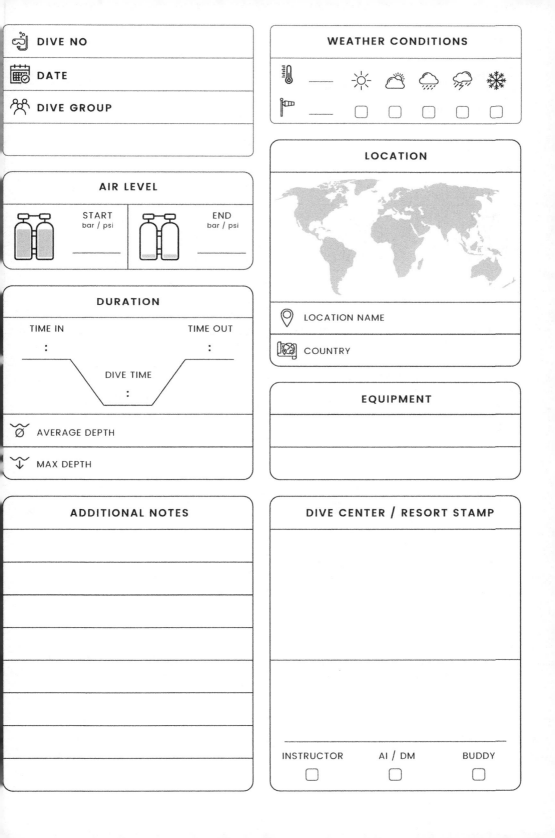

LOCATION NAME

COUNTRY

EQUIPMENT

ADDITIONAL NOTES

DIVE CENTER / RESORT STAMP

INSTRUCTOR

AI / DM

BUDDY

DIVE NO

DATE

DIVE GROUP

WEATHER CONDITIONS

AIR LEVEL

START
bar / psi

END
bar / psi

DURATION

TIME IN

TIME OUT

:

:

DIVE TIME

:

AVERAGE DEPTH

MAX DEPTH

LOCATION

LOCATION NAME

COUNTRY

EQUIPMENT

ADDITIONAL NOTES

DIVE CENTER / RESORT STAMP

INSTRUCTOR

AI / DM

BUDDY

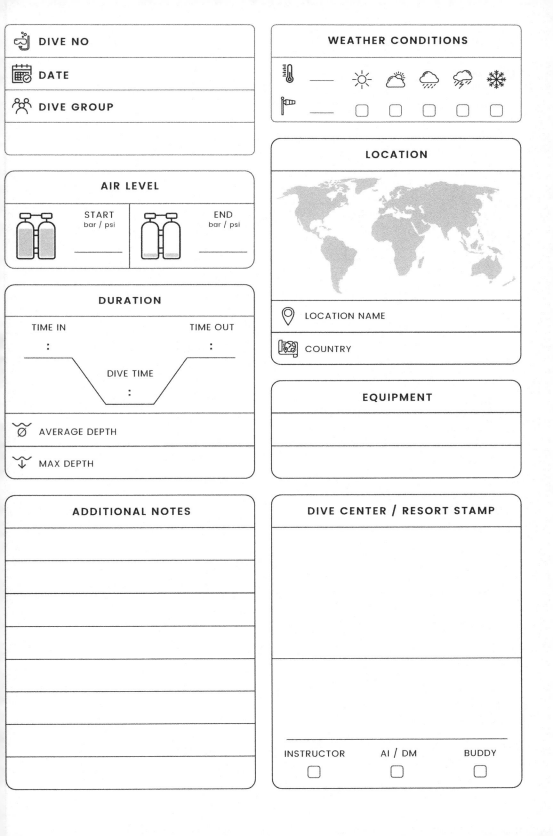

DIVE NO

DATE

DIVE GROUP

WEATHER CONDITIONS

AIR LEVEL

START
bar / psi

END
bar / psi

DURATION

TIME IN

TIME OUT

:

:

DIVE TIME

:

AVERAGE DEPTH

MAX DEPTH

LOCATION

LOCATION NAME

COUNTRY

EQUIPMENT

ADDITIONAL NOTES

DIVE CENTER / RESORT STAMP

INSTRUCTOR

AI / DM

BUDDY

DIVE NO

DATE

DIVE GROUP

WEATHER CONDITIONS

AIR LEVEL

	START bar / psi		END bar / psi

DURATION

TIME IN   TIME OUT

:   :

DIVE TIME

:

AVERAGE DEPTH

MAX DEPTH

LOCATION

LOCATION NAME

COUNTRY

EQUIPMENT

ADDITIONAL NOTES

DIVE CENTER / RESORT STAMP

INSTRUCTOR   AI / DM   BUDDY

DIVE NO

DATE

DIVE GROUP

WEATHER CONDITIONS

AIR LEVEL

START bar / psi	END bar / psi

DURATION

TIME IN :   TIME OUT :

DIVE TIME :

AVERAGE DEPTH

MAX DEPTH

LOCATION

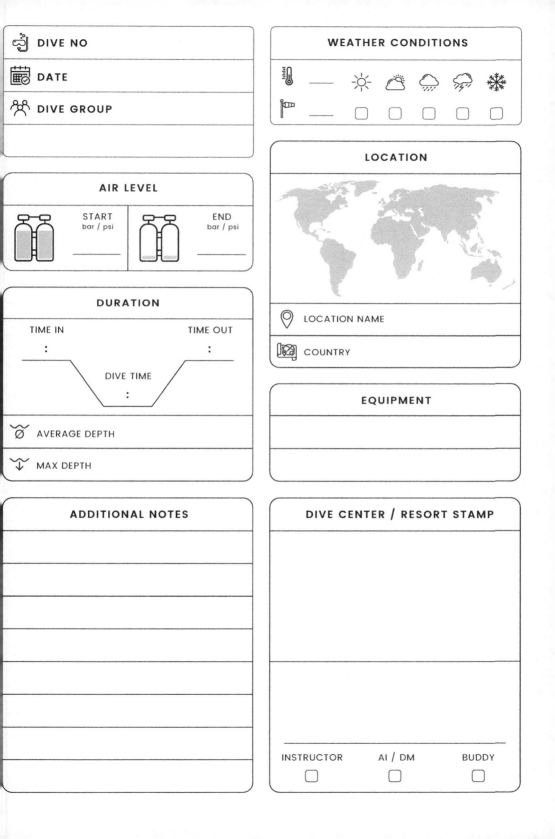

LOCATION NAME

COUNTRY

EQUIPMENT

ADDITIONAL NOTES

DIVE CENTER / RESORT STAMP

INSTRUCTOR   AI / DM   BUDDY

DIVE NO

DATE

DIVE GROUP

WEATHER CONDITIONS

AIR LEVEL

| START bar / psi | END bar / psi |

LOCATION

LOCATION NAME

COUNTRY

DURATION

TIME IN

:

TIME OUT

:

DIVE TIME

:

AVERAGE DEPTH

MAX DEPTH

EQUIPMENT

ADDITIONAL NOTES

DIVE CENTER / RESORT STAMP

INSTRUCTOR

AI / DM

BUDDY

DIVE NO

DATE

DIVE GROUP

WEATHER CONDITIONS

AIR LEVEL

START
bar / psi

END
bar / psi

LOCATION

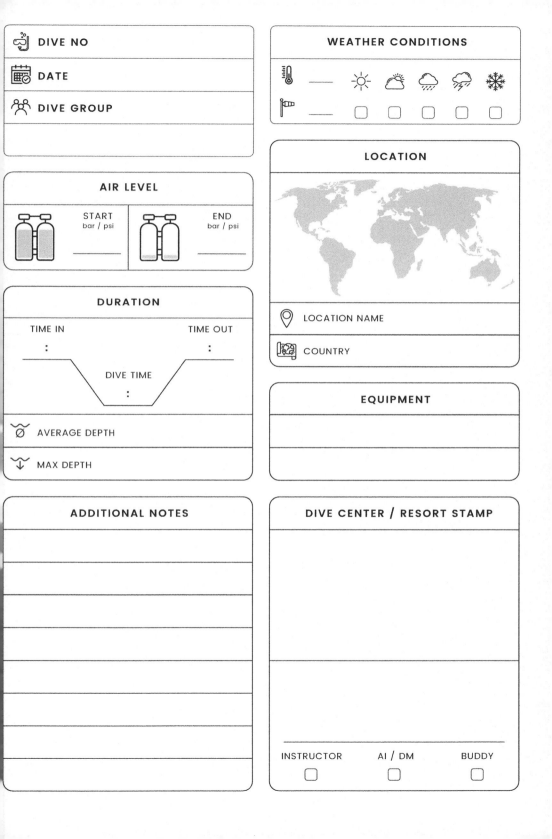

LOCATION NAME

COUNTRY

DURATION

TIME IN

TIME OUT

:

:

DIVE TIME

:

AVERAGE DEPTH

MAX DEPTH

EQUIPMENT

ADDITIONAL NOTES

DIVE CENTER / RESORT STAMP

INSTRUCTOR

AI / DM

BUDDY

DIVE NO

DATE

DIVE GROUP

WEATHER CONDITIONS

AIR LEVEL

START bar / psi	END bar / psi

DURATION

TIME IN

TIME OUT

:

:

DIVE TIME

:

AVERAGE DEPTH

MAX DEPTH

LOCATION

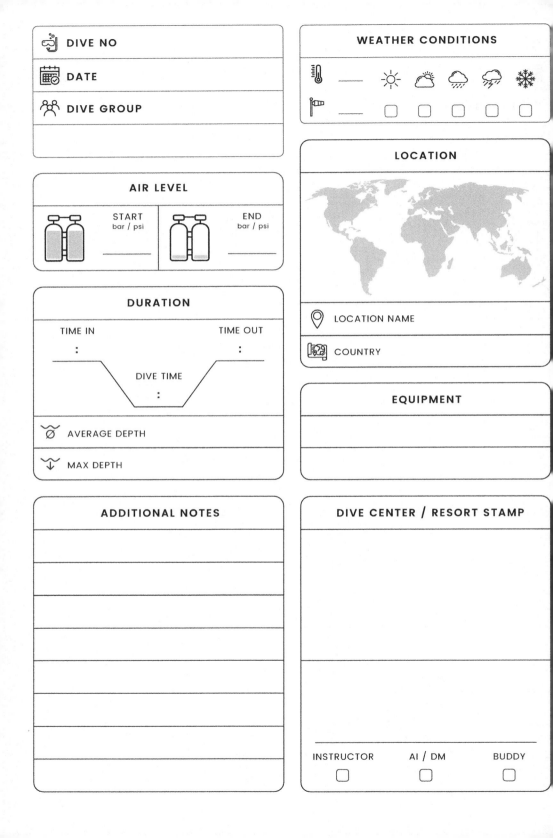

LOCATION NAME

COUNTRY

EQUIPMENT

ADDITIONAL NOTES

DIVE CENTER / RESORT STAMP

INSTRUCTOR

AI / DM

BUDDY

DIVE NO

DATE

DIVE GROUP

WEATHER CONDITIONS

AIR LEVEL

START
bar / psi

END
bar / psi

DURATION

TIME IN

TIME OUT

:

:

DIVE TIME

:

AVERAGE DEPTH

MAX DEPTH

LOCATION

LOCATION NAME

COUNTRY

EQUIPMENT

ADDITIONAL NOTES

DIVE CENTER / RESORT STAMP

INSTRUCTOR

AI / DM

BUDDY

DIVE NO

DATE

DIVE GROUP

WEATHER CONDITIONS

AIR LEVEL

START bar / psi	END bar / psi

DURATION

TIME IN :   TIME OUT :

DIVE TIME :

AVERAGE DEPTH

MAX DEPTH

LOCATION

LOCATION NAME

COUNTRY

EQUIPMENT

ADDITIONAL NOTES

DIVE CENTER / RESORT STAMP

INSTRUCTOR	AI / DM	BUDDY

DIVE NO

DATE

DIVE GROUP

WEATHER CONDITIONS

AIR LEVEL

	START bar / psi		END bar / psi
	_____		_____

LOCATION

LOCATION NAME

COUNTRY

DURATION

TIME IN

TIME OUT

:

:

DIVE TIME

:

AVERAGE DEPTH

MAX DEPTH

EQUIPMENT

ADDITIONAL NOTES

DIVE CENTER / RESORT STAMP

INSTRUCTOR   AI / DM   BUDDY

DIVE NO

DATE

DIVE GROUP

WEATHER CONDITIONS

AIR LEVEL

START bar / psi	END bar / psi

DURATION

TIME IN   TIME OUT

:   :

DIVE TIME

:

AVERAGE DEPTH

MAX DEPTH

LOCATION

LOCATION NAME

COUNTRY

EQUIPMENT

ADDITIONAL NOTES

DIVE CENTER / RESORT STAMP

INSTRUCTOR   AI / DM   BUDDY

DIVE NO

DATE

DIVE GROUP

WEATHER CONDITIONS

AIR LEVEL

	START bar / psi		END bar / psi

DURATION

TIME IN   TIME OUT

:   :

DIVE TIME

:

AVERAGE DEPTH

MAX DEPTH

LOCATION

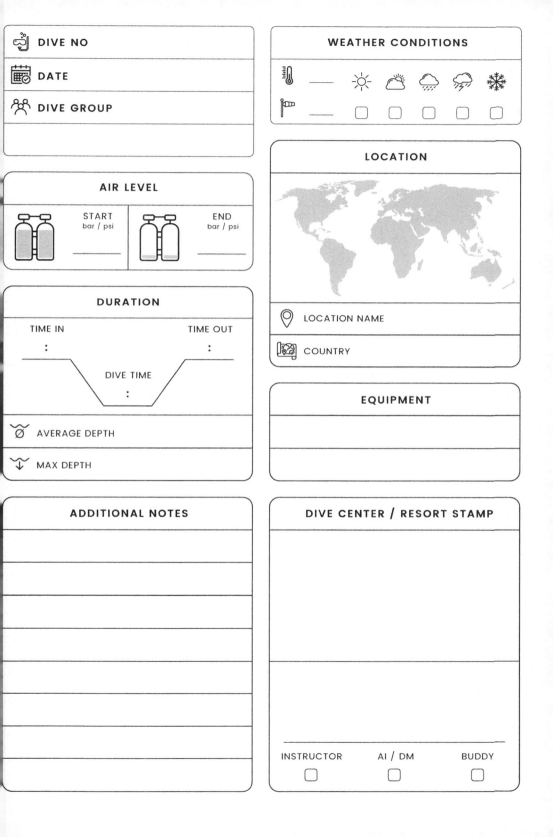

LOCATION NAME

COUNTRY

EQUIPMENT

ADDITIONAL NOTES

DIVE CENTER / RESORT STAMP

INSTRUCTOR   AI / DM   BUDDY

DIVE NO

DATE

DIVE GROUP

WEATHER CONDITIONS

AIR LEVEL

START bar / psi	END bar / psi

DURATION

TIME IN :

TIME OUT :

DIVE TIME :

AVERAGE DEPTH

MAX DEPTH

LOCATION

LOCATION NAME

COUNTRY

EQUIPMENT

ADDITIONAL NOTES

DIVE CENTER / RESORT STAMP

INSTRUCTOR

AI / DM

BUDDY

DIVE NO

DATE

DIVE GROUP

WEATHER CONDITIONS

AIR LEVEL

START
bar / psi

END
bar / psi

DURATION

TIME IN

TIME OUT

:

:

DIVE TIME

:

AVERAGE DEPTH

MAX DEPTH

LOCATION

LOCATION NAME

COUNTRY

EQUIPMENT

ADDITIONAL NOTES

DIVE CENTER / RESORT STAMP

INSTRUCTOR

AI / DM

BUDDY

DIVE NO

DATE

DIVE GROUP

WEATHER CONDITIONS

AIR LEVEL

START
bar / psi

END
bar / psi

DURATION

TIME IN

TIME OUT

:

:

DIVE TIME

:

AVERAGE DEPTH

MAX DEPTH

LOCATION

LOCATION NAME

COUNTRY

EQUIPMENT

ADDITIONAL NOTES

DIVE CENTER / RESORT STAMP

INSTRUCTOR

AI / DM

BUDDY

DIVE NO

DATE

DIVE GROUP

WEATHER CONDITIONS

AIR LEVEL

START
bar / psi

END
bar / psi

DURATION

TIME IN

TIME OUT

:

:

DIVE TIME

:

AVERAGE DEPTH

MAX DEPTH

LOCATION

LOCATION NAME

COUNTRY

EQUIPMENT

ADDITIONAL NOTES

DIVE CENTER / RESORT STAMP

INSTRUCTOR

AI / DM

BUDDY

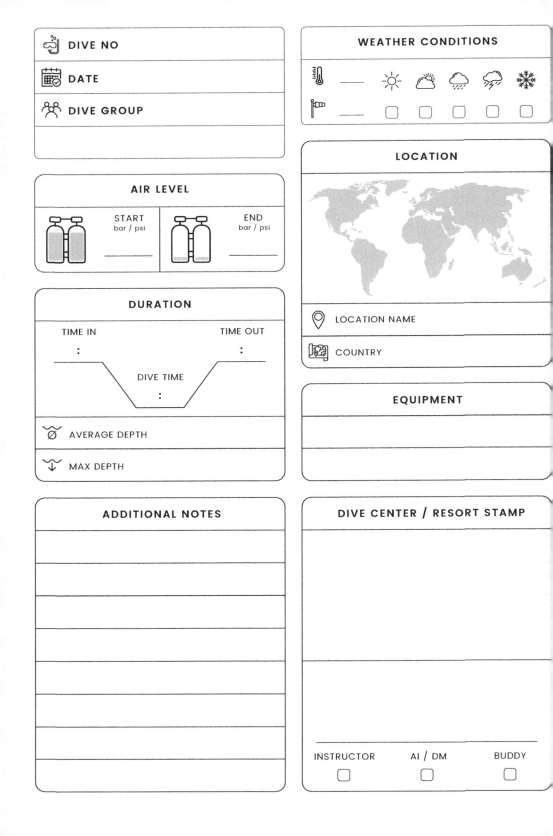

DIVE NO

DATE

DIVE GROUP

AIR LEVEL

START
bar / psi

_____

END
bar / psi

_____

DURATION

TIME IN

:

TIME OUT

:

DIVE TIME

:

AVERAGE DEPTH

MAX DEPTH

WEATHER CONDITIONS

LOCATION

LOCATION NAME

COUNTRY

EQUIPMENT

ADDITIONAL NOTES

DIVE CENTER / RESORT STAMP

INSTRUCTOR

AI / DM

BUDDY

DIVE NO

DATE

DIVE GROUP

WEATHER CONDITIONS

AIR LEVEL

START
bar / psi

END
bar / psi

DURATION

TIME IN

TIME OUT

:

:

DIVE TIME

:

AVERAGE DEPTH

MAX DEPTH

LOCATION

LOCATION NAME

COUNTRY

EQUIPMENT

ADDITIONAL NOTES

DIVE CENTER / RESORT STAMP

INSTRUCTOR

AI / DM

BUDDY

DIVE NO

DATE

DIVE GROUP

WEATHER CONDITIONS

AIR LEVEL

START
bar / psi

END
bar / psi

DURATION

TIME IN

TIME OUT

:

:

DIVE TIME

:

AVERAGE DEPTH

MAX DEPTH

LOCATION

LOCATION NAME

COUNTRY

EQUIPMENT

ADDITIONAL NOTES

DIVE CENTER / RESORT STAMP

INSTRUCTOR

AI / DM

BUDDY

DIVE NO

DATE

DIVE GROUP

WEATHER CONDITIONS

AIR LEVEL

START
bar / psi

END
bar / psi

DURATION

TIME IN

TIME OUT

:

:

DIVE TIME

:

AVERAGE DEPTH

MAX DEPTH

LOCATION

LOCATION NAME

COUNTRY

EQUIPMENT

ADDITIONAL NOTES

DIVE CENTER / RESORT STAMP

INSTRUCTOR

AI / DM

BUDDY

DIVE NO

DATE

DIVE GROUP

WEATHER CONDITIONS

AIR LEVEL

START bar / psi	END bar / psi

DURATION

TIME IN   TIME OUT

:   :

DIVE TIME

:

AVERAGE DEPTH

MAX DEPTH

LOCATION

LOCATION NAME

COUNTRY

EQUIPMENT

ADDITIONAL NOTES

DIVE CENTER / RESORT STAMP

INSTRUCTOR   AI / DM   BUDDY

DIVE NO

DATE

DIVE GROUP

WEATHER CONDITIONS

AIR LEVEL

START
bar / psi

END
bar / psi

DURATION

TIME IN

TIME OUT

:

:

DIVE TIME

:

AVERAGE DEPTH

MAX DEPTH

LOCATION

LOCATION NAME

COUNTRY

EQUIPMENT

ADDITIONAL NOTES

DIVE CENTER / RESORT STAMP

INSTRUCTOR

AI / DM

BUDDY

DIVE NO

DATE

DIVE GROUP

WEATHER CONDITIONS

AIR LEVEL

START bar / psi	END bar / psi
____	____

DURATION

TIME IN   TIME OUT

:   :

DIVE TIME

:

AVERAGE DEPTH

MAX DEPTH

LOCATION

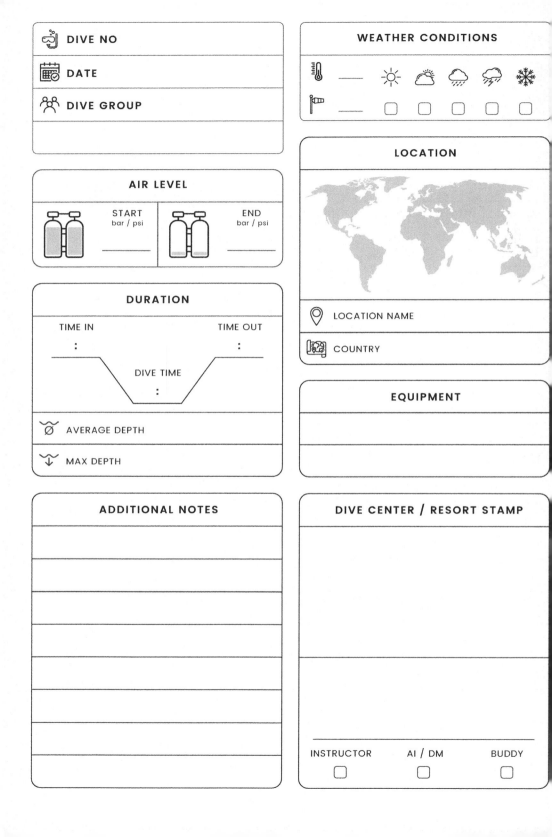

LOCATION NAME

COUNTRY

EQUIPMENT

ADDITIONAL NOTES

DIVE CENTER / RESORT STAMP

INSTRUCTOR   AI / DM   BUDDY

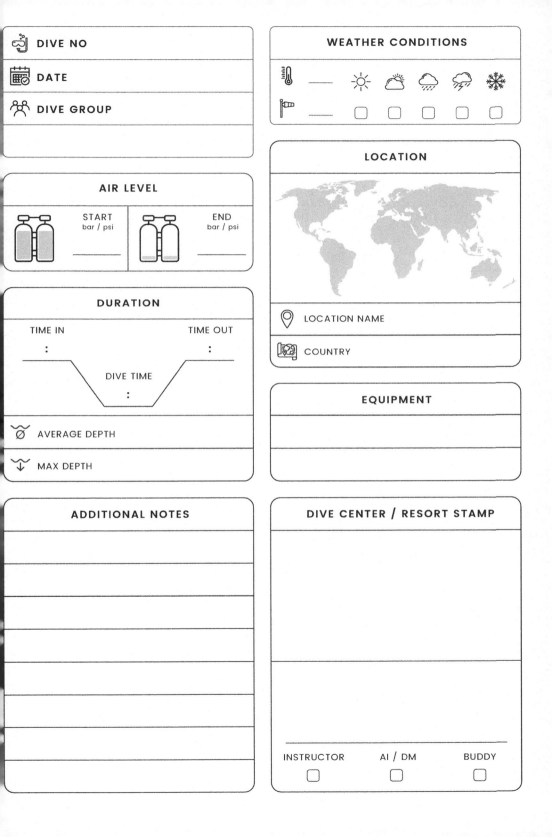

DIVE NO

DATE

DIVE GROUP

WEATHER CONDITIONS

AIR LEVEL

START
bar / psi

END
bar / psi

DURATION

TIME IN

TIME OUT

:

:

DIVE TIME

:

AVERAGE DEPTH

MAX DEPTH

LOCATION

LOCATION NAME

COUNTRY

EQUIPMENT

ADDITIONAL NOTES

DIVE CENTER / RESORT STAMP

INSTRUCTOR

AI / DM

BUDDY

DIVE NO

DATE

DIVE GROUP

WEATHER CONDITIONS

AIR LEVEL

START bar / psi	END bar / psi
_____	_____

DURATION

TIME IN   TIME OUT

:   :

DIVE TIME

:

AVERAGE DEPTH

MAX DEPTH

LOCATION

LOCATION NAME

COUNTRY

EQUIPMENT

ADDITIONAL NOTES

DIVE CENTER / RESORT STAMP

INSTRUCTOR   AI / DM   BUDDY

DIVE NO

DATE

DIVE GROUP

WEATHER CONDITIONS

AIR LEVEL

START
bar / psi

END
bar / psi

DURATION

TIME IN

TIME OUT

:

:

DIVE TIME

:

AVERAGE DEPTH

MAX DEPTH

LOCATION

LOCATION NAME

COUNTRY

EQUIPMENT

ADDITIONAL NOTES

DIVE CENTER / RESORT STAMP

INSTRUCTOR

AI / DM

BUDDY

DIVE NO

DATE

DIVE GROUP

WEATHER CONDITIONS

AIR LEVEL

START bar / psi	END bar / psi

DURATION

TIME IN   TIME OUT

:   :

DIVE TIME

:

AVERAGE DEPTH

MAX DEPTH

LOCATION

LOCATION NAME

COUNTRY

EQUIPMENT

ADDITIONAL NOTES

DIVE CENTER / RESORT STAMP

INSTRUCTOR   AI / DM   BUDDY

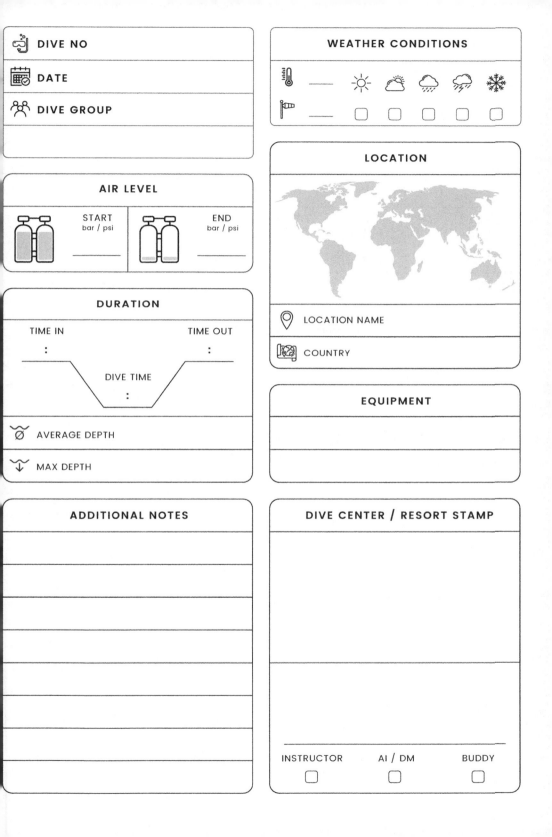

DIVE NO

DATE

DIVE GROUP

WEATHER CONDITIONS

AIR LEVEL

START
bar / psi

END
bar / psi

DURATION

TIME IN

TIME OUT

:

:

DIVE TIME

:

AVERAGE DEPTH

MAX DEPTH

LOCATION

LOCATION NAME

COUNTRY

EQUIPMENT

ADDITIONAL NOTES

DIVE CENTER / RESORT STAMP

INSTRUCTOR

AI / DM

BUDDY

DIVE NO

DATE

DIVE GROUP

WEATHER CONDITIONS

AIR LEVEL

START bar / psi	END bar / psi

LOCATION

LOCATION NAME

COUNTRY

DURATION

TIME IN :   TIME OUT :

DIVE TIME :

AVERAGE DEPTH

MAX DEPTH

EQUIPMENT

ADDITIONAL NOTES

DIVE CENTER / RESORT STAMP

INSTRUCTOR   AI / DM   BUDDY

DIVE NO

DATE

DIVE GROUP

WEATHER CONDITIONS

AIR LEVEL

START
bar / psi

END
bar / psi

DURATION

TIME IN

TIME OUT

:

:

DIVE TIME

:

AVERAGE DEPTH

MAX DEPTH

LOCATION

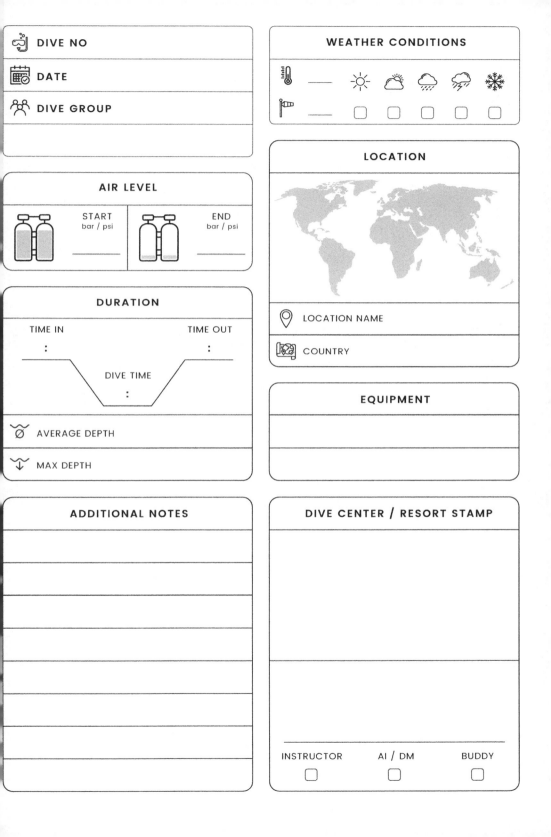

LOCATION NAME

COUNTRY

EQUIPMENT

ADDITIONAL NOTES

DIVE CENTER / RESORT STAMP

INSTRUCTOR

AI / DM

BUDDY

DIVE NO

DATE

DIVE GROUP

WEATHER CONDITIONS

AIR LEVEL

	START bar / psi		END bar / psi

DURATION

TIME IN   TIME OUT

:   :

DIVE TIME

:

AVERAGE DEPTH

MAX DEPTH

LOCATION

LOCATION NAME

COUNTRY

EQUIPMENT

ADDITIONAL NOTES

DIVE CENTER / RESORT STAMP

INSTRUCTOR   AI / DM   BUDDY

DIVE NO

DATE

DIVE GROUP

WEATHER CONDITIONS

AIR LEVEL

START bar / psi	END bar / psi
_____	_____

DURATION

TIME IN   TIME OUT

:   :

DIVE TIME

:

AVERAGE DEPTH

MAX DEPTH

LOCATION

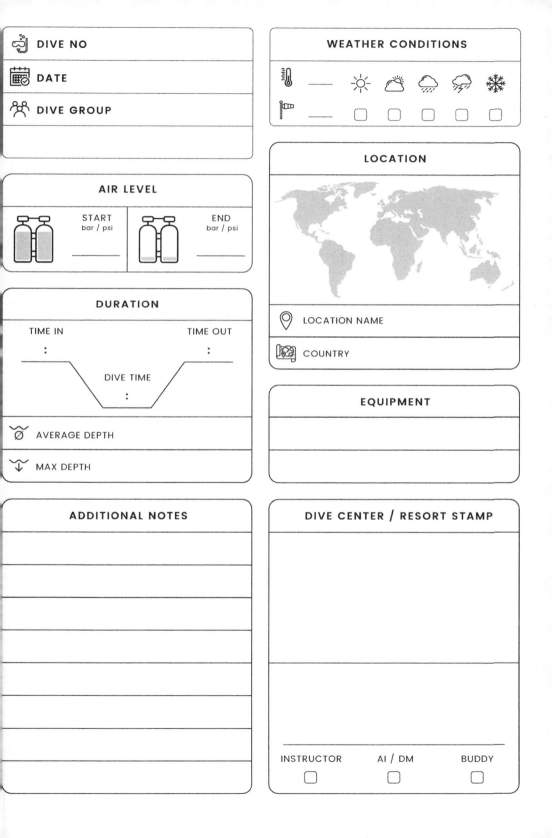

LOCATION NAME

COUNTRY

EQUIPMENT

ADDITIONAL NOTES

DIVE CENTER / RESORT STAMP

INSTRUCTOR   AI / DM   BUDDY

DIVE NO

DATE

DIVE GROUP

WEATHER CONDITIONS

AIR LEVEL

| START bar / psi | END bar / psi |

LOCATION

LOCATION NAME

COUNTRY

DURATION

TIME IN   TIME OUT

:   :

DIVE TIME

:

AVERAGE DEPTH

MAX DEPTH

EQUIPMENT

ADDITIONAL NOTES

DIVE CENTER / RESORT STAMP

INSTRUCTOR   AI / DM   BUDDY

DIVE NO

DATE

DIVE GROUP

WEATHER CONDITIONS

AIR LEVEL

START bar / psi	END bar / psi

DURATION

TIME IN

:

TIME OUT

:

DIVE TIME

:

AVERAGE DEPTH

MAX DEPTH

LOCATION

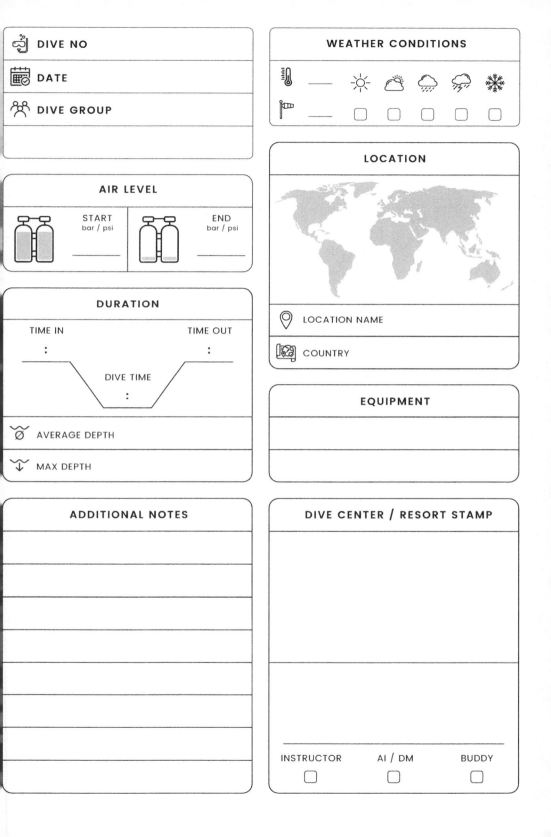

LOCATION NAME

COUNTRY

EQUIPMENT

ADDITIONAL NOTES

DIVE CENTER / RESORT STAMP

INSTRUCTOR

AI / DM

BUDDY

DIVE NO

DATE

DIVE GROUP

WEATHER CONDITIONS

AIR LEVEL

START bar / psi	END bar / psi

DURATION

TIME IN

TIME OUT

:

:

DIVE TIME

:

AVERAGE DEPTH

MAX DEPTH

LOCATION

LOCATION NAME

COUNTRY

EQUIPMENT

ADDITIONAL NOTES

DIVE CENTER / RESORT STAMP

INSTRUCTOR

AI / DM

BUDDY

DIVE NO

DATE

DIVE GROUP

WEATHER CONDITIONS

AIR LEVEL

START
bar / psi

END
bar / psi

DURATION

TIME IN

TIME OUT

:

:

DIVE TIME

:

AVERAGE DEPTH

MAX DEPTH

LOCATION

LOCATION NAME

COUNTRY

EQUIPMENT

ADDITIONAL NOTES

DIVE CENTER / RESORT STAMP

INSTRUCTOR

AI / DM

BUDDY

DIVE NO

DATE

DIVE GROUP

WEATHER CONDITIONS

AIR LEVEL

START bar / psi	END bar / psi

LOCATION

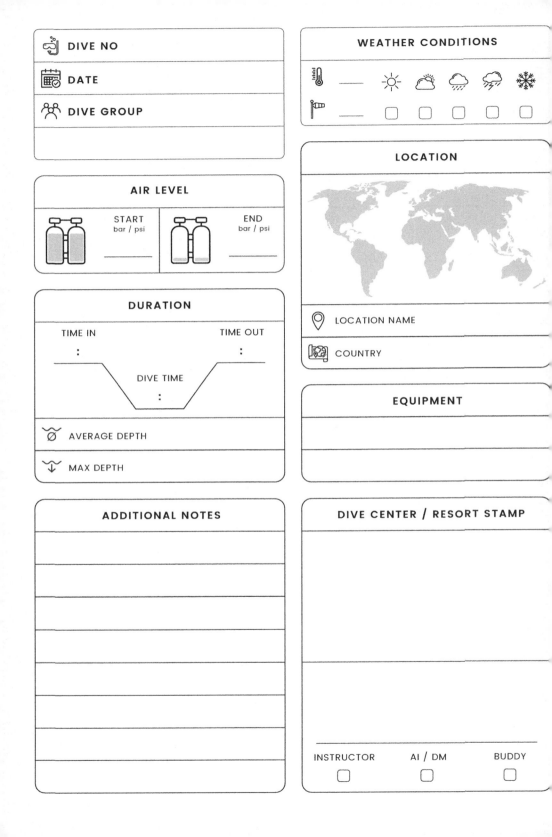

LOCATION NAME

COUNTRY

DURATION

TIME IN

TIME OUT

DIVE TIME

AVERAGE DEPTH

MAX DEPTH

EQUIPMENT

ADDITIONAL NOTES

DIVE CENTER / RESORT STAMP

INSTRUCTOR   AI / DM   BUDDY

DIVE NO

DATE

DIVE GROUP

WEATHER CONDITIONS

AIR LEVEL

START
bar / psi

END
bar / psi

DURATION

TIME IN

TIME OUT

:

:

DIVE TIME

:

AVERAGE DEPTH

MAX DEPTH

LOCATION

LOCATION NAME

COUNTRY

EQUIPMENT

ADDITIONAL NOTES

DIVE CENTER / RESORT STAMP

INSTRUCTOR

AI / DM

BUDDY

DIVE NO

DATE

DIVE GROUP

WEATHER CONDITIONS

AIR LEVEL

START bar / psi	END bar / psi

DURATION

TIME IN

TIME OUT

:

:

DIVE TIME

:

AVERAGE DEPTH

MAX DEPTH

LOCATION

LOCATION NAME

COUNTRY

EQUIPMENT

ADDITIONAL NOTES

DIVE CENTER / RESORT STAMP

INSTRUCTOR

AI / DM

BUDDY

DIVE NO

DATE

DIVE GROUP

WEATHER CONDITIONS

AIR LEVEL

START
bar / psi

END
bar / psi

DURATION

TIME IN

TIME OUT

:

:

DIVE TIME

:

AVERAGE DEPTH

MAX DEPTH

LOCATION

LOCATION NAME

COUNTRY

EQUIPMENT

ADDITIONAL NOTES

DIVE CENTER / RESORT STAMP

INSTRUCTOR

AI / DM

BUDDY

DIVE NO

DATE

DIVE GROUP

WEATHER CONDITIONS

AIR LEVEL

| START bar / psi | END bar / psi |

LOCATION

LOCATION NAME

COUNTRY

DURATION

TIME IN

:

TIME OUT

:

DIVE TIME

:

AVERAGE DEPTH

MAX DEPTH

EQUIPMENT

ADDITIONAL NOTES

DIVE CENTER / RESORT STAMP

INSTRUCTOR   AI / DM   BUDDY

DIVE NO

DATE

DIVE GROUP

WEATHER CONDITIONS

AIR LEVEL

START
bar / psi

_____

END
bar / psi

_____

LOCATION

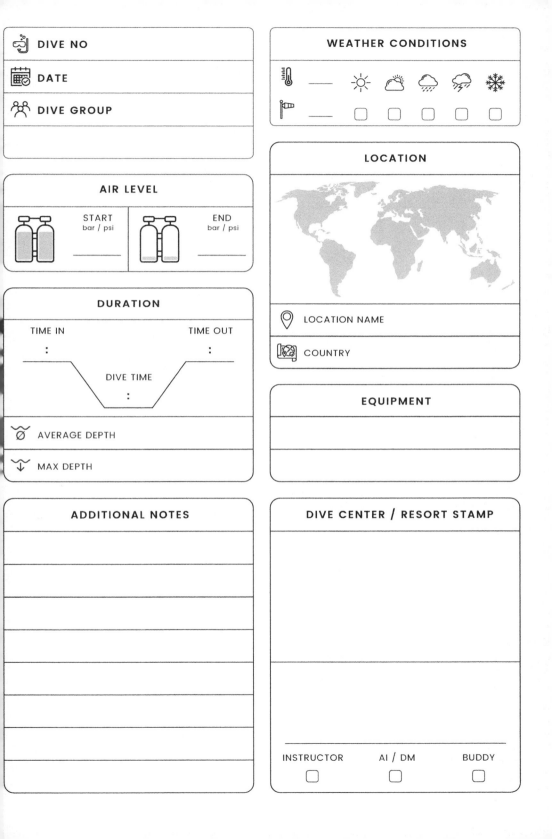

LOCATION NAME

COUNTRY

DURATION

TIME IN

:

TIME OUT

:

DIVE TIME

:

AVERAGE DEPTH

MAX DEPTH

EQUIPMENT

ADDITIONAL NOTES

DIVE CENTER / RESORT STAMP

INSTRUCTOR

AI / DM

BUDDY

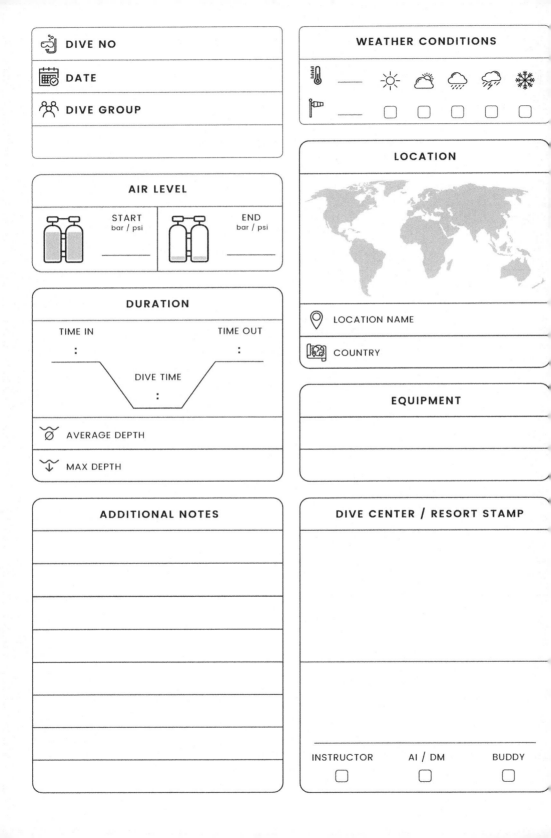

DIVE NO

DATE

DIVE GROUP

AIR LEVEL

START
bar / psi

END
bar / psi

DURATION

TIME IN

TIME OUT

:

:

DIVE TIME

:

AVERAGE DEPTH

MAX DEPTH

WEATHER CONDITIONS

LOCATION

LOCATION NAME

COUNTRY

EQUIPMENT

ADDITIONAL NOTES

DIVE CENTER / RESORT STAMP

INSTRUCTOR

AI / DM

BUDDY

DIVE NO

DATE

DIVE GROUP

WEATHER CONDITIONS

AIR LEVEL

START
bar / psi

END
bar / psi

DURATION

TIME IN

TIME OUT

:

:

DIVE TIME

:

AVERAGE DEPTH

MAX DEPTH

LOCATION

LOCATION NAME

COUNTRY

EQUIPMENT

ADDITIONAL NOTES

DIVE CENTER / RESORT STAMP

INSTRUCTOR

AI / DM

BUDDY

DIVE NO

DATE

DIVE GROUP

WEATHER CONDITIONS

AIR LEVEL

START bar / psi	END bar / psi

DURATION

TIME IN   TIME OUT

:   :

DIVE TIME

:

AVERAGE DEPTH

MAX DEPTH

LOCATION

LOCATION NAME

COUNTRY

EQUIPMENT

ADDITIONAL NOTES

DIVE CENTER / RESORT STAMP

INSTRUCTOR   AI / DM   BUDDY

DIVE NO

DATE

DIVE GROUP

WEATHER CONDITIONS

AIR LEVEL

START
bar / psi

END
bar / psi

DURATION

TIME IN

TIME OUT

:

:

DIVE TIME

:

AVERAGE DEPTH

MAX DEPTH

LOCATION

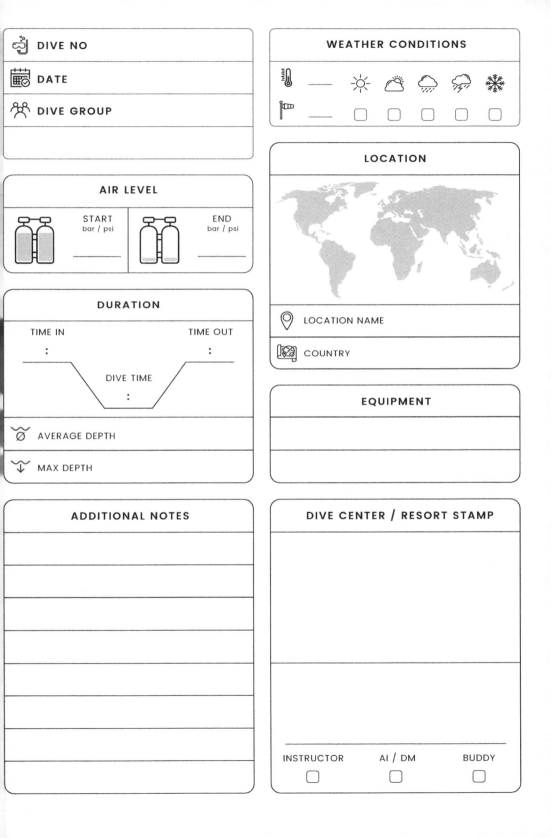

LOCATION NAME

COUNTRY

EQUIPMENT

ADDITIONAL NOTES

DIVE CENTER / RESORT STAMP

INSTRUCTOR

AI / DM

BUDDY

DIVE NO

DATE

DIVE GROUP

WEATHER CONDITIONS

AIR LEVEL

START bar / psi	END bar / psi

LOCATION

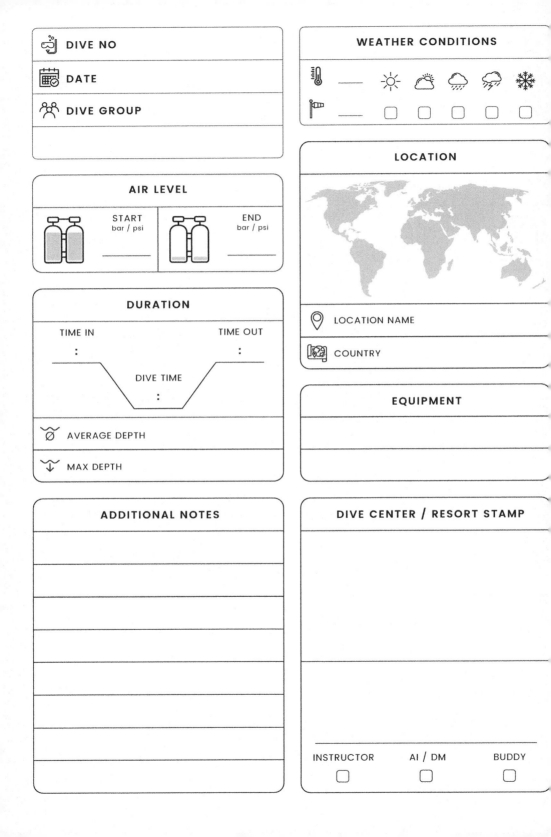

LOCATION NAME

COUNTRY

DURATION

TIME IN

TIME OUT

:

:

DIVE TIME

:

AVERAGE DEPTH

MAX DEPTH

EQUIPMENT

ADDITIONAL NOTES

DIVE CENTER / RESORT STAMP

INSTRUCTOR

AI / DM

BUDDY

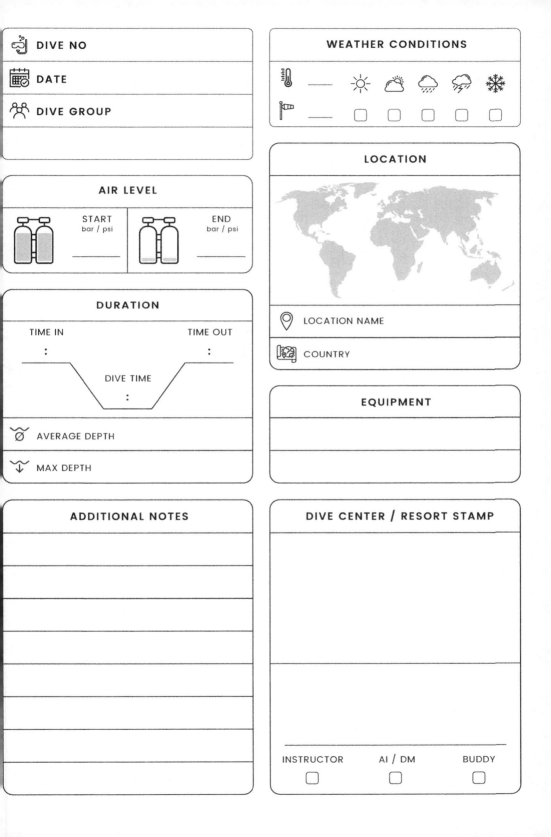

DIVE NO

DATE

DIVE GROUP

AIR LEVEL

START
bar / psi

END
bar / psi

DURATION

TIME IN

TIME OUT

:

:

DIVE TIME

:

AVERAGE DEPTH

MAX DEPTH

WEATHER CONDITIONS

LOCATION

LOCATION NAME

COUNTRY

EQUIPMENT

ADDITIONAL NOTES

DIVE CENTER / RESORT STAMP

INSTRUCTOR

AI / DM

BUDDY

DIVE NO

DATE

DIVE GROUP

WEATHER CONDITIONS

AIR LEVEL

START bar / psi	END bar / psi

DURATION

TIME IN   TIME OUT

:   :

DIVE TIME

:

AVERAGE DEPTH

MAX DEPTH

LOCATION

LOCATION NAME

COUNTRY

EQUIPMENT

ADDITIONAL NOTES

DIVE CENTER / RESORT STAMP

INSTRUCTOR   AI / DM   BUDDY

DIVE NO

DATE

DIVE GROUP

WEATHER CONDITIONS

AIR LEVEL

START
bar / psi

END
bar / psi

DURATION

TIME IN

TIME OUT

:

:

DIVE TIME

:

AVERAGE DEPTH

MAX DEPTH

LOCATION

LOCATION NAME

COUNTRY

EQUIPMENT

ADDITIONAL NOTES

DIVE CENTER / RESORT STAMP

INSTRUCTOR

AI / DM

BUDDY

DIVE NO

DATE

DIVE GROUP

WEATHER CONDITIONS

AIR LEVEL

START
bar / psi
_____

END
bar / psi
_____

DURATION

TIME IN
:

TIME OUT
:

DIVE TIME
:

AVERAGE DEPTH

MAX DEPTH

LOCATION

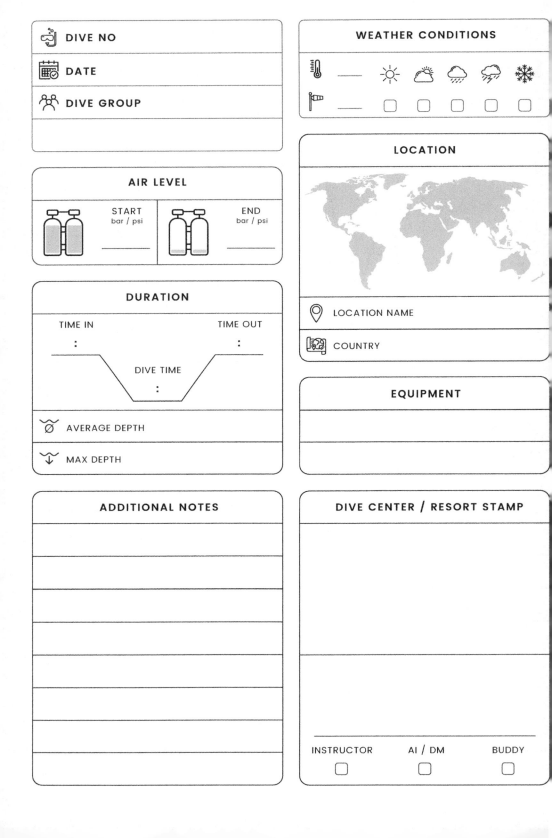

LOCATION NAME

COUNTRY

EQUIPMENT

ADDITIONAL NOTES

DIVE CENTER / RESORT STAMP

INSTRUCTOR

AI / DM

BUDDY

DIVE NO

DATE

DIVE GROUP

WEATHER CONDITIONS

AIR LEVEL

START
bar / psi

END
bar / psi

DURATION

TIME IN

TIME OUT

:

:

DIVE TIME

:

AVERAGE DEPTH

MAX DEPTH

LOCATION

LOCATION NAME

COUNTRY

EQUIPMENT

ADDITIONAL NOTES

DIVE CENTER / RESORT STAMP

INSTRUCTOR

AI / DM

BUDDY

DIVE NO

DATE

DIVE GROUP

AIR LEVEL

START bar / psi	END bar / psi

DURATION

TIME IN

TIME OUT

:

:

DIVE TIME

:

AVERAGE DEPTH

MAX DEPTH

ADDITIONAL NOTES

WEATHER CONDITIONS

LOCATION

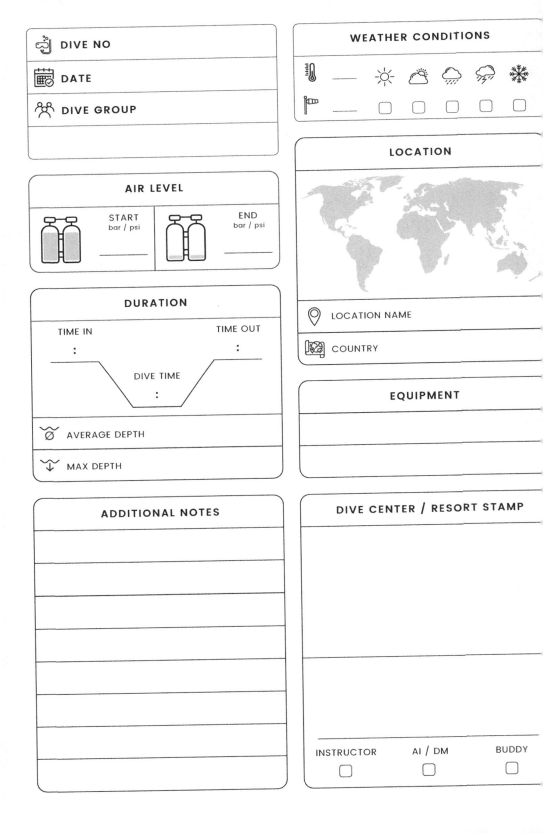

LOCATION NAME

COUNTRY

EQUIPMENT

DIVE CENTER / RESORT STAMP

INSTRUCTOR

AI / DM

BUDDY

DIVE NO

DATE

DIVE GROUP

WEATHER CONDITIONS

AIR LEVEL

START bar / psi	END bar / psi

DURATION

TIME IN   TIME OUT
:   :

DIVE TIME
:

AVERAGE DEPTH

MAX DEPTH

LOCATION

LOCATION NAME

COUNTRY

EQUIPMENT

ADDITIONAL NOTES

DIVE CENTER / RESORT STAMP

INSTRUCTOR   AI / DM   BUDDY

DIVE NO

DATE

DIVE GROUP

WEATHER CONDITIONS

AIR LEVEL

START bar / psi	END bar / psi

DURATION

TIME IN   TIME OUT

:   :

DIVE TIME

:

AVERAGE DEPTH

MAX DEPTH

LOCATION

LOCATION NAME

COUNTRY

EQUIPMENT

ADDITIONAL NOTES

DIVE CENTER / RESORT STAMP

INSTRUCTOR   AI / DM   BUDDY

DIVE NO

DATE

DIVE GROUP

WEATHER CONDITIONS

AIR LEVEL

	START bar / psi		END bar / psi
	_____		_____

DURATION

TIME IN   TIME OUT

:   :

DIVE TIME

:

AVERAGE DEPTH

MAX DEPTH

LOCATION

LOCATION NAME

COUNTRY

EQUIPMENT

ADDITIONAL NOTES

DIVE CENTER / RESORT STAMP

INSTRUCTOR   AI / DM   BUDDY

DIVE NO

DATE

DIVE GROUP

WEATHER CONDITIONS

AIR LEVEL

START bar / psi	END bar / psi

DURATION

TIME IN :   TIME OUT :

DIVE TIME :

AVERAGE DEPTH

MAX DEPTH

LOCATION

LOCATION NAME

COUNTRY

EQUIPMENT

ADDITIONAL NOTES

DIVE CENTER / RESORT STAMP

INSTRUCTOR   AI / DM   BUDDY

DIVE NO

DATE

DIVE GROUP

WEATHER CONDITIONS

AIR LEVEL

START
bar / psi

END
bar / psi

DURATION

TIME IN

TIME OUT

:

:

DIVE TIME

:

AVERAGE DEPTH

MAX DEPTH

LOCATION

LOCATION NAME

COUNTRY

EQUIPMENT

ADDITIONAL NOTES

DIVE CENTER / RESORT STAMP

INSTRUCTOR

AI / DM

BUDDY

DIVE NO

DATE

DIVE GROUP

WEATHER CONDITIONS

AIR LEVEL

START bar / psi	END bar / psi
_____	_____

DURATION

TIME IN

TIME OUT

:

:

DIVE TIME

:

AVERAGE DEPTH

MAX DEPTH

LOCATION

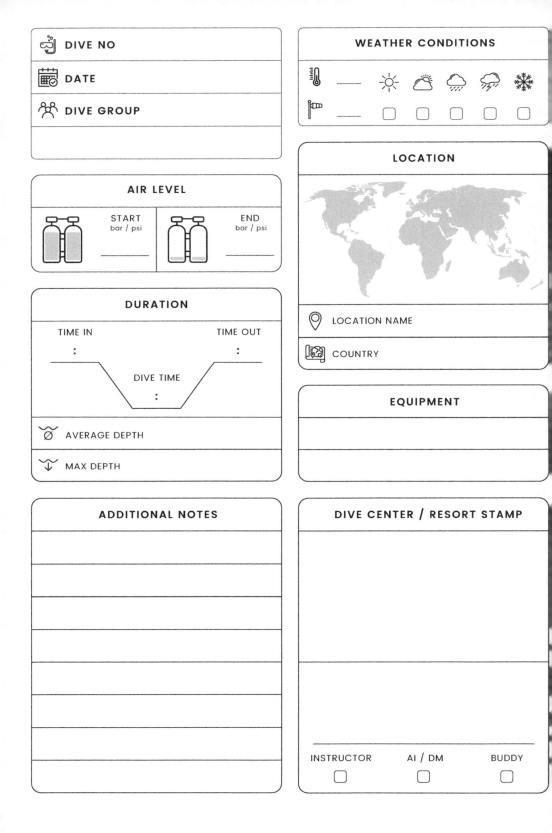

LOCATION NAME

COUNTRY

EQUIPMENT

ADDITIONAL NOTES

DIVE CENTER / RESORT STAMP

INSTRUCTOR   AI / DM   BUDDY

DIVE NO

DATE

DIVE GROUP

WEATHER CONDITIONS

—

—

AIR LEVEL

START bar / psi	END bar / psi
_____	_____

DURATION

TIME IN   TIME OUT

:   :

DIVE TIME

:

AVERAGE DEPTH

MAX DEPTH

LOCATION

LOCATION NAME

COUNTRY

EQUIPMENT

ADDITIONAL NOTES

DIVE CENTER / RESORT STAMP

INSTRUCTOR   AI / DM   BUDDY

DIVE NO

DATE

DIVE GROUP

WEATHER CONDITIONS

AIR LEVEL

START	END
bar / psi	bar / psi

DURATION

TIME IN

TIME OUT

:

:

DIVE TIME

:

AVERAGE DEPTH

MAX DEPTH

LOCATION

LOCATION NAME

COUNTRY

EQUIPMENT

ADDITIONAL NOTES

DIVE CENTER / RESORT STAMP

INSTRUCTOR   AI / DM   BUDDY

DIVE NO

DATE

DIVE GROUP

WEATHER CONDITIONS

AIR LEVEL

| START | END |
| bar / psi | bar / psi |

DURATION

TIME IN — TIME OUT

: :

DIVE TIME

:

AVERAGE DEPTH

MAX DEPTH

LOCATION

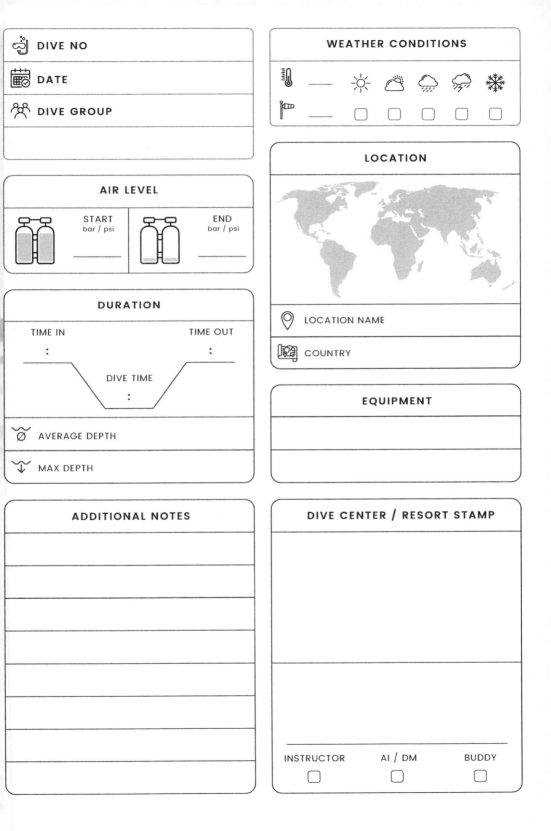

LOCATION NAME

COUNTRY

EQUIPMENT

ADDITIONAL NOTES

DIVE CENTER / RESORT STAMP

INSTRUCTOR   AI / DM   BUDDY

DIVE NO

DATE

DIVE GROUP

WEATHER CONDITIONS

AIR LEVEL

START bar / psi	END bar / psi

DURATION

TIME IN

TIME OUT

:

:

DIVE TIME

:

AVERAGE DEPTH

MAX DEPTH

LOCATION

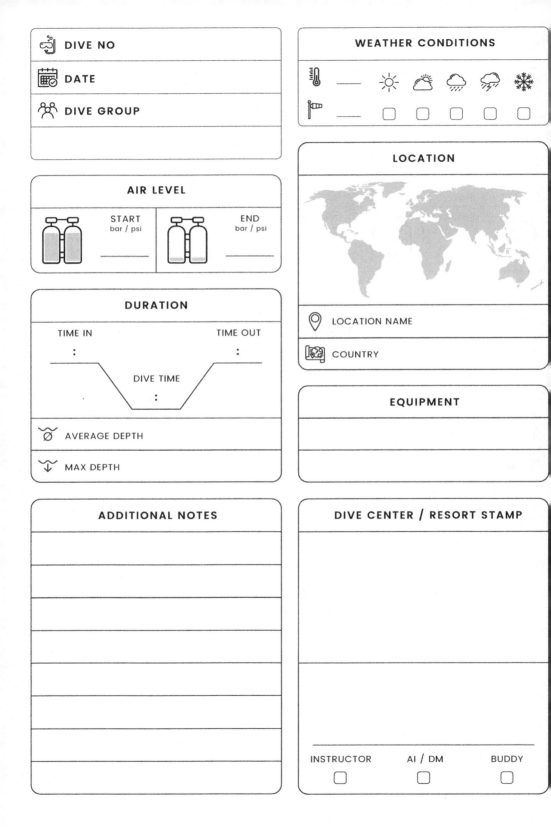

LOCATION NAME

COUNTRY

EQUIPMENT

ADDITIONAL NOTES

DIVE CENTER / RESORT STAMP

INSTRUCTOR	AI / DM	BUDDY